Grade 6

W9-AQJ-441

Grammar
PRACTICE BOOK

Macmillan
McGraw-Hill

B

The *McGraw·Hill* Companies

**Macmillan
McGraw-Hill**

Published by Macmillan/McGraw-Hill, of McGraw-Hill Education, a division of The McGraw-Hill Companies, Inc.,
Two Penn Plaza, New York, New York 10121.

Printed in the United States of America

8 9 10 024 09 08

Contents

Unit 2 • Saving the Day

Unit 3 • Great Ideas

Unit 4 • Achievements

© Macmillan/McGraw-Hill

Unit 5 • Turning Points

Unit 6 • Yesterday, Today, and Tomorrow

Name_____

- A **sentence** is a group of words that expresses a complete thought. Every sentence begins with a capital letter.
- A **sentence fragment** does not express a complete thought.
- A **declarative sentence** makes a statement. It ends with a period.
- An **interrogative sentence** asks a question. It ends with a question mark.

Read each sentence or phrase below. Write S beside it if it is a sentence. Write F if it is a fragment. Then add words to the fragments so that they express complete thoughts.

1. Toni and Beth went hiking in the woods yesterday.

   _____

2. Lost their way.

   _____

3. Forgot flashlights and water.

   _____

4. Why did their parents allow them to go?

   _____

5. Luckily for the girls.

   _____

   _____

Put the correct punctuation mark at the end of each sentence.

6. Name several safety tips for hiking and climbing

7. Wearing proper clothing and footwear are basic tips

8. Why is it important to carry water

9. Penny wants to know more about camping

10. Why must climbers sign up before beginning their climb

© Macmillan/McGraw-Hill

At Home: Ask the student to write five declarative sentences and five interrogative sentences.

The Summer of the Swans

Grade 6/Unit 1   **1**

Name_____

> • An **imperative sentence** gives a command or makes a request. It ends with a period.
> • An **exclamatory sentence** expresses strong feeling. It ends with an exclamation point.

Read each sentence. Write whether it is *declarative, interrogative, imperative,* or *exclamatory*.

1. What a wonderful camping trip that was!

_____

2. Think about what Peter said about staying safe on a hike.

_____

3. How many times have you climbed in the Shawangunk Mountains?

_____

4. Don't delay getting down the mountain before sunset.

_____

5. Richard couldn't decide whether or not to go.

_____

6. I'm so excited to be on this hike!

_____

Revise the first four sentences. Change them to either interrogative or declarative sentences.

7. _____

8. _____

_____

9. _____

_____

10. _____

_____

At Home: Ask the student to write a declarative, an interrogative, an imperative, and an exclamatory sentence.

Name _____

> • Capitalize the first word of every sentence.
> • End each sentence with the correct punctuation mark—
>   a period, a question mark, or an exclamation point.

Correct the capitalization or punctuation of each sentence. Then identify the sentence type in the space provided.

1. Talk to Tiana about food to bring on the trip?

_____

2. what a beautiful sight Mohonk Mountain is!

_____

3. Why must he always complain about his aching back!

_____

4. the Shawangunk Mountains are in New York state.

_____

5. Bring your cell phone on the trip tomorrow?

_____

6. hiking is great exercise.

_____

7. How long will we be gone.

_____

8. Don't expect to be home before 8:00 P.M.!

_____

9. go to sleep early the night before the hike!

_____

10. We will be leaving at 5:00 A.M.?

_____

© Macmillan/McGraw-Hill

At Home: Have the student write an interrogative sentence, and a response with an imperative sentence.

Name_____

- Begin a new sentence with a capital letter.
- **Declarative sentences** and **imperative sentences** end with a period.
- **Interrogative sentences** end with a question mark.
- **Exclamatory sentences** end with an exclamation point.

Rewrite the passage, correcting all capitalization and punctuation mistakes.

i am so happy that rescue teams are on alert at all times to come to the aid of stranded or lost hikers i recently attended one of the classes teams hold to help campers think ahead about unexpected situations what if someone in my group became ill or injured what kind of weather conditions might I expect do I have the skills necessary to safely complete the trip I plan to make these questions never occurred to me

_____

_____

_____

_____

_____

_____

_____

_____

_____

_____

At Home: Invite the student to write a personal narrative about a trip he or she has made.

Name_____

Add to the beginning of each group of words so that it forms a sentence. The information in parentheses will tell you what type of sentence it should be. Be sure to begin each sentence with a capital letter and end it with the correct punctuation mark.

1. each hiker from the nature group (declarative)

   _____

2. know the location of the nearest ranger station (interrogative)

   _____

3. embarrassing to the group (exclamatory)

   _____

   _____

4. extra food and clothing (imperative)

   _____

5. good idea to have an extra map (declarative)

   _____

6. a mother bear (exclamatory)

   _____

7. with her buddy Tasha, (declarative)

   _____

   _____

8. know they were such good friends (interrogative)

   _____

9. can check your supplies (imperative)

   _____

   _____

10. never shows up late (declarative)

   _____

Name_____

- A **sentence** is a group of words that expresses a complete thought.

- There are four types of sentences: **declarative, interrogative, imperative,** and **exclamatory.**

Write four sentences that have something to do with rescue efforts or camping and hiking. Make one sentence declarative, one interrogative, one imperative, and one exclamatory. When you are finished, read the sentences to a partner. Talk about how your voice helps identify the different types of sentences.

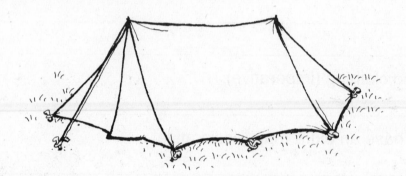

1. _____

_____

2. _____

_____

3. _____

_____

4. _____

_____

Name

- The **complete subject** includes all the words that tell what or whom the sentence is about.
- The **simple subject** is the main word or words in the complete subject.
- You can sometimes correct a sentence fragment by adding a subject.

Read each sentence. Write the complete subject on the line provided below each example. Put parentheses ( ) around the simple subject. (In some sentences, the complete subject and the simple subject may be the same.)

1. The ruins of many ancient cities are located in Mexico.

_____

2. The Mexican people live and work near ancient archaeological sites.

_____

3. My cousin Isabel is studying to become an archaeologist.

_____

4. The large capital of Mexico is her home.

_____

5. Isabel hopes to travel to Tulum sometime soon with her classmates.

_____

6. The entire class will be guided on the trip by a well-known scientist.

_____

7. The students are looking forward to seeing some real artifacts.

_____

8. The department's leading professor has arranged the trip.

_____

© Macmillan/McGraw-Hill

At Home: Have the student write about a trip he or she has made. Then have him or her locate the simple and complete subjects.

Lost City • Grade 6/Unit I   7

Name_____

- The **complete predicate** includes all the words that tell what the subject does or is.
- The **simple predicate** is the main word or words in the complete predicate.
- You can sometimes correct a sentence fragment by adding a predicate.

Read each sentence. Write the complete predicate on the space provided below each example. Put parentheses around the simple predicate. (In some sentences, the complete predicate and the simple predicate may be the same.)

1. Isabel learns languages as part of her schoolwork in archaeology.

_____

_____

2. She and her classmates practice their English with each other.

_____

3. Sometimes at home Isabel speaks English or French.

_____

4. She even knows a little Chinese!

_____

5. The dean of the language department at Isabel's university approves.

_____

6. Chinese is a difficult language to learn.

_____

7. She works hard to master the characters.

_____

8. Late into the night, Isabel is often studying.

_____

At Home: Have the student write about a subject he or she enjoys. Then have him or her locate the simple and complete predicates.

Name _____

> • Begin the greeting and closing of a letter with a capital letter.
> • Use a comma after the greeting and closing of a friendly letter.
> • Use a comma between the names of a city and a state.
> • Use a comma between the day and year in a date.

Proofread this friendly letter for errors in commas and capitalization. Add commas as necessary. Cross out the letters that should be capitalized.

> 1723 Carolyn Lane
>
> Orlando FL 32819
>
> June 1 2006

dear Lupe

Let me tell you about my fabulous trip to Mexico! I took an archaeological tour with my family through the Yucatan Peninsula. We learned about the great Maya civilization and saw the ruins of many of their cities. The Maya had a calendar and written language. They also studied the planets and stars.

Our trip began on May 5 2006 and we did not get home until Memorial Day! The weather in Mexico was perfect for hiking the ruins, and the beaches of Cancun were fantastic. I learned how to snorkel, and Danny saw a barracuda! Coming home to Orlando Florida may seem a lot less exciting, but it's good to be back.

> your friend
>
> Marisa

At Home: Have the student write a friendly letter to someone he or she knows or would like to meet.

Name_____

> • Begin the greeting and closing of a letter with a capital letter.
> • Use a comma after the greeting and closing of a friendly letter.
> • Use a comma between the names of a city and a state.
> • Use a comma between the day and year in a date.

Proofread the letter Ivelise wrote to her cousin Isabel. Add commas as necessary. Cross out incorrect punctuation and the letters that should be capitalized. Use correct punctuation.

1800 Fortune Avenue

Tampa FL 33624

December 11 2006

dear Isabel

I received your letter last week, but I've been quite busy. Do you remember I told you about my history class. Well, we are learning about ancient cities like the ones you have been visiting

My homework load is heavy, but I am enjoying learning about the South American cities? Are the Maya people like the ancient Inca people I am learning about. I wish you were here so you could help me with this essay I have to write?

write soon and tell me about your trip to the Yucatan. My mom says we may be coming to Mexico City to visit soon. I can't wait to show you my photos.

your cousin

Ivelise

At Home: Have the student write about one of his or her favorite cities. Urge your student to write complete sentences.

Name_____

Decide which word or group of words is the sentence part named in parentheses. Circle the letter of your answer.

1. My cousin Lupe enjoyed her visit to Key West, Florida. (simple subject)

　a. enjoyed her visit

　b. enjoyed

　c. My cousin Lupe

　d. Lupe

2. She visited many of the historic sites around the city. (complete predicate)

　a. She visited

　b. visited many of the historic sites around the city

　c. around the city

　d. many of the historic sites

3. Lupe gradually felt more at home in the city. (simple predicate)

　a. felt

　b. gradually felt more at home

　c. at home in the city

　d. Lupe gradually

4. An exhausting day of travel can make anyone feel tired. (complete subject)

　a. day of travel

　b. An exhausting day of travel

　c. anyone

　d. can make anyone feel tired

5. A nice cup of tea usually makes Lupe feel a lot better. (simple subject)

　a. A nice cup of tea

　b. a lot better

　c. makes Lupe feel

　d. cup

Name_____

- The **complete subject** includes all the words that tell what or whom the sentence is about. The **simple subject** is the main word or words in the complete subject.
- The **complete predicate** includes all the words that tell what the subject does or is. The **simple predicate** is the main word or words in the complete predicate.
- You can sometimes correct a sentence fragment by adding a subject or predicate.

Write a friendly letter to someone you know that tells about a trip you have taken, or would like to take, to a lost city. Make sure each sentence contains a subject and a predicate. When you are finished, read the letter to a partner. Identify the complete and simple subjects and predicates in each sentence.

_____

_____

_____

_____

_____

_____

_____

_____

_____

_____

_____

_____

Name_____

- A **conjunction** joins words or groups of words. *And* adds information; *but* shows contrast; *or* gives a choice.
- A **compound sentence** contains two sentences joined by a comma and *and*, *but*, or *or*.
- You can form a compound sentence by joining two related sentences.

Put an X in front of each sentence that is a compound sentence. For those sentences, write the word that joins the two shorter sentences.

1. _____ Crayons were invented in 1903 by Edwin Binney and Harold Smith, and they were an instant success.

    _____

2. _____ Crossword puzzles can be diamond-shaped, or they can be square.

    _____

3. _____ The first ferriswheel began operating on June 21, 1893 at the Chicago World's Fair.

    _____

4. _____ It had 36 wooden cars that could each seat 40 people, but most modern ferriswheels are much smaller.

    _____

5. _____ A kaleidoscope is a tube one can look into that makes beautiful, colorful patterns using mirrors.

    _____

6. _____ The kaleidoscope was invented by the Scottish physicist Sir David Brewster in 1817.

    _____

© Macmillan/McGraw-Hill

At Home: Ask the student to write each compound sentence as two separate sentences.

Gecko Glue, Cockroach Scouts, and Spider Silk Bridges • **Grade 6/Unit 1**

13

Name_____

- A **compound subject** contains two or more simple subjects that have the same predicate.
- A **compound predicate** contains two or more simple predicates that have the same subject.
- You can combine two sentences by joining two subjects or two predicates with *and, but,* or *or.*

Read the sentences. Write an *S* if it has a compound subject and *P* if it has a compoud predicate. Write each compound subject and compound predicate below. Then put parentheses around the simple subjects or predicates in what you have written. (Not every sentence has a compound subject or compound predicate.)

1. My older sister, Selina, is studying hard and hopes to be an inventor one day. _____

_____

_____

2. Calculus, physics, and chemistry are her favorite subjects. _____

_____

3. My preferred subject has always been English literature. _____

_____

4. Selina rises early and arrives home late. _____

_____

5. Selina's teachers and classmates believe she is marked for fame and fortune. _____

_____

6. A big title and huge corner office are of no interest to Selina. _____

_____

Gecko Glue, Cockroach Scouts, and
Spider Silk Bridges • **Grade 6/Unit 1**

At Home: Have your student write about his or her intended future profession. Two sentences should contain a compound subject.

- Use a comma before the conjunction in a compound sentence.
- If two parts of a compound sentence are not joined by a conjunction, a semicolon is used to separate the parts.

Combine each set of sentences. Use a comma and a conjunction in the compound sentence.

1. Tic Tac Toe has been played in the United Kingdom for hundreds of years. There it is called Noughts and Crosses.

_____

_____

2. A.S. Douglas was the first to put Noughts and Crosses on a software program. That was way back in 1949!

_____

_____

3. In 1956, Noah and Joe McVicker invented play dough. It was promoted as a wallpaper cleaner first.

_____

_____

4. Joe realized the child-safe type of clay would make a great toy. He became a millionaire almost overnight.

_____

_____

5. Over 700 million pounds of play dough have been sold since it was first marketed. The formula is still a secret.

_____

_____

© Macmillan/McGraw-Hill

At Home: Have the student come up with simple sentences on a topic. Then have him or her combine them into compound sentences.

Gecko Glue, Cockroach Scouts, and Spider Silk Bridges • **Grade 6/Unit I**

15

Name_____

> • Use a comma before the conjunction in a compound sentence.
> • If two parts of a compound sentence are not joined by a conjunction, use a semicolon to separate the parts.

Rewrite the passage below, correcting all capitalization and punctation mistakes. Combine any sentences you find appropriate.

everyone knows that necessity is the mother of invention the woman who invented disposable diapers was both a woman and an inventor Marion Donovan invented the disposable diaper in 1950 she used a regular cloth diaper, lined it with pieces cut from a shower curtain, and called her invention "Boaters" since no company was interested in marketing her new invention Mrs. Donovan founded her own company today disposable diapers are big business

_____

_____

_____

_____

_____

_____

_____

At Home: Invite the student to write a short paragraph about his or her favorite everyday invention.

Name_____

Revise the following paragraph so that it reads more clearly. Combine short sentences with a conjunction to form compound subjects, compound predicates, or compound sentences. Not every sentence needs to be combined or revised.

People put on their clothing every day. They do not think about how their pants stay put. They do not think about how their jackets stay put. Jackets have zippers. Pants have zippers. The zipper was invented in 1893 by Whitcomb L. Judson. He called his invention a "clasp-locker." In 1923, Mr. B.F. Goodrich coined the word "zipper." His company made rubber boots with zippers. His company sold rubber boots with zippers. Mr. Goodrich named them zippers because they made a zipping sound when opened and closed.

_____
_____
_____
_____
_____
_____
_____
_____
_____
_____
_____
_____
_____

Name_____

> • You can combine two related sentences by using a conjunction. You can also combine two sentences by joining two subjects or two predicates with *and, but,* or *or.*
> • Use a comma before the conjunction in a compound sentence. If two parts of a compound sentence are not joined by a conjunction, use a semicolon to separate the parts.

Rewrite the following sets of sentences. Create a compound sentence or sentences with compound subjects or predicates. Use the correct punctuation.

1. Eleven-year-old Frank Epperson invented the frozen fruit pop in 1905. He didn't mean to do it.

_____

_____

2. Epperson was enjoying a fruit drink. He left it out overnight with the stirrer still in it.

_____

_____

3. The fruit drink froze. It certainly made a delicious new treat.

_____

_____

4. Young Frank patented his "frozen ice on a stick" in 1923. He originally called his invention the Epsicle.

_____

_____

5. Epperson thought Epsicle was a great name. The frozen treat was later renamed.

_____

_____

Name_____

- A **clause** is a group of words with a subject and a predicate.
- An **independent clause** can stand alone as a sentence.
- A **dependent clause** cannot stand alone as a sentence.
- A **dependent clause** begins with a conjunction such as *wherever, before, while, because, as if,* or *unless.*

Read each group of words. Write I beside each independent clause. Write D beside each dependent clause. Then rewrite each dependent clause so that it is part of a sentence.

_____ **1.** Whenever I read a story.

_____

_____

_____ **2.** Because I enjoy them.

_____

_____ **3.** Jasmine is the most talented writer in our class.

_____

_____ **4.** Although she hopes to be a published writer.

_____

_____ **5.** Jasmine would like to study communications as well.

_____

_____ **6.** Because her grandmother used to tell her folk tales.

_____

_____ **7.** She would sit on her grandmother's lap and listen to her great stories.

_____

_____ **8.** Jasmine hopes to one day write a story like her grandmother's.

_____

At Home: Have the student write five dependent clauses. Then have him or her complete them.

- A **complex sentence** contains an independent clause and one or more dependent clauses.
- When a dependent clause comes at the beginning of a sentence, use a comma after the dependent clause.
- When a dependent clause comes at the end, a comma is not usually necessary.

Put an X in front of each complex sentence. If the dependent clause comes at the end of the sentence, rewrite the sentence so that the dependent clause comes at the beginning. If the dependent clause comes at the beginning of the sentence, rewrite it so that it comes at the end. (Note: not every sentence is complex.)

_____ **1.** While I read, I often listen to soft music.

_____

_____ **2.** I have yet to find my folk tale in the library.

_____

_____ **3.** I usually carry a book with me wherever I go.

_____

_____ **4.** I probably will not be happy until I finish reading every book on my shelf.

_____

_____ **5.** My sister is always calling me a book worm.

_____

_____ **6.** Before I left for school this morning, I read a tale of a brave knight.

_____

_____ **7.** I forgot what time it was until my mother called me.

_____

_____ **8.** I find folk tales interesting because of the history in them.

_____

© Macmillan/McGraw-Hill

At Home: Ask the student to write a short paragraph on a popular folk tale. It should contain at least two complex sentences.

Name_____

- When a dependent clause comes at the beginning of a sentence, use a comma after the dependent clause.
- When a dependent clause comes at the end, a comma is not usually necessary.

Read the following interview. Rewrite each line, adding commas to the dialogue where they are needed. Remove any unnecessary commas.

REPORTER: When your first novel was published were you nervous?

_____

_____

FAMOUS WRITER: On the contrary I felt elated.

_____

_____

REPORTER: As you work, on your next book do you find yourself writing to please your readers?

_____

_____

FAMOUS WRITER: No, I always write to please myself because I write what I feel, and believe.

_____

_____

At Home: Challenge the student to write a short poem on a topic of his or her choosing.

- A **complex sentence** contains an independent clause and one or more dependent clauses.
- When a dependent clause comes at the beginning of a sentence, use a comma after the dependent clause.
- When a dependent clause comes at the end, you usually do not use a comma.

Rewrite the passage. Draw a line under the complex sentences. Correct the capitalization and punctuation mistakes, adding punctuation as needed.

every family has its own traditions, but ours is my favorite on Sunday nights we all sit around the kitchen table with a bowl of roasted walnuts hazelnuts peanuts, and almonds as we crack the nuts each family member tells one good thing and one bad thing that happened to them that week this family time not only teaches us about each other but also lets us see that things are never all that bad

_____

_____

_____

_____

_____

_____

_____

_____

At Home: Invite the student to write a paragraph about a family tradition. Tell him or her to use at least two complex sentences.

Name_____

Each question begins with a sentence that, when joined with the correct response, will result in a complex sentence. Circle the letter of your answer. Hint: The correct answer will be a clause.

1. We have an unusual family tradition at our house

  a. every night.

  b. when tired.

  c. that every family should adopt.

2. Every Memorial Day, we have a family fire drill

  a. that my parents carefully organize.

  b. and barbeque.

  c. only once.

3. every person knows what to do and where to go.

  a. Today

  b. If a fire starts,

  c. In this case,

Try making sentences from the different answers. Choose the answer that gives you a complex sentence with correct punctuation. Circle the letter of your answer.

4. Isaac takes little Maria by the hand

  a. first of all.

  b. for safety sake.

  c. before he walks her safely across the street.

5. Everyone meets on the neighbors' lawn

  a. that night.

  b. so we can have a big barbeque.

  c. across the street.

Name_____

> - A **complex sentence** contains an independent clause and one or more dependent clauses.
> - When a dependent clause comes at the beginning of a sentence, use a comma after the dependent clause.
> - When a dependent clause comes at the end, a comma is not usually necessary.

Study the picture and think about a folk tale it might describe. Read the following groups of words. Add phrases to turn the four groups of words into four complex sentences. Be sure to use commas correctly in your sentences.

1. Although everyone knew the hare could run very fast

_____

_____

2. Because the tortoise was known for being so slow

_____

_____

3. Because tortoises are patient

_____

_____

4. If the hare became too sure of himself

_____

_____

Name

- A **run-on sentence** joins together two or more sentences that should be written separately.
- You can correct a run-on sentence by separating two complete ideas into two sentences.

Put an X in front of each run-on sentence. Then correct the sentences in the space provided.

_____ 1. The kiwi bird is a strange-looking animal it is part of a group of endangered species.

_____

_____

_____ 2. These animals have died or been killed in such large numbers that there are very few left.

_____

_____

_____ 3. The kiwi's body is covered with fluffy feathers unlike other birds, the kiwi has no tail.

_____

_____

_____ 4. Kiwis are the size of a chicken their eggs are as large as ostriches' eggs!

_____

_____

_____ 5. The kiwi's "cousin," the dodo bird, is already extinct.

_____

_____ 6. There are no dodos left anywhere in the world no other dodos will ever be born.

_____

_____

© Macmillan/McGraw-Hill

At Home: Have the student write four run-on sentences and then rewrite each one as two separate sentences.

Name_____

- A **run-on sentence** may be rewritten as a compound or complex sentence or separated into two sentences.

Read these sentences. If the sentence is correct, write C on the line next to it. If it is a run-on sentence, write R. Rewrite each run-on sentence.

_____ **1.** The platypus has feet like a duck's.

_____

_____ **2.** Many scientists have studied the platypus dark brown fur covers its body.

_____

_____

_____ **3.** Platypuses live on land, although these odd animals also swim very well.

_____

_____ **4.** The female platypus lays eggs the mother sits on the eggs like a bird.

_____

_____

_____ **5.** The platypus has survived for millions of years many scientists call it a living fossil.

_____

_____

_____ **6.** Unlike ducks platypuses have bills that are soft and feel for food underwater.

_____

_____

_____ **7.** Australia is the home of the platypus it prefers fresh water to the salt water that surrounds the island.

_____

_____

At Home: Have the student revise his or her sentences again, this time using different methods.

© Macmillan/McGraw-Hill

Name_____

- A **sentence fragment** does not express a complete thought. You can sometimes correct a sentence fragment by adding a subject or predicate.
- Use a comma before the conjunction in a compound sentence. If there is no conjunction, use a semicolon.
- Use a comma after a dependent clause at the beginning of a sentence.

Rewrite each run-on sentence or sentence fragment using proper capitalization, commas, and end punctuation.

1. scientists study wildlife in order to protect it the study of the cheetah is an example

_____

2. is found mainly in northern Africa

_____

3. its feet have hard pads with sharp edges these special pads help the cheetah to grip the ground

_____

_____

4. the cheetah has been called a natural running machine it is able to reach a speed of 71 miles per hour

_____

_____

5. it may be the fastest animal on Earth we must protect this amazing cat

_____

_____

6. the cheetah is an endangered species it is even extinct in India and northern Africa

_____

_____

© Macmillan/McGraw-Hill

At Home: Challenge the student to do the activity again, trying different methods of revision.

Interrupted Journey • **Grade 6/Unit 1** 27

- A **sentence fragment** does not express a complete thought. You can sometimes correct a sentence fragment by adding a subject or predicate.
- A **run-on sentence** joins together two or more sentences that should be written separately.
- You can correct run-on sentences in three different ways:
  1. Separate two complete ideas in a run-on sentence into two sentences.
  2. Rewrite the run-on sentence as a compound sentence.
  3. Rewrite the run-on sentence as a complex sentence.

Correct any sentence fragments or run-on sentences in the diary entry below. Rewrite the passage with correct punctuation and capitalization.

today I joined a group of students on a bird-watching walk i wanted to see a snail kite because I read that this bird is in trouble the snail kite eats only one thing it eats the meat of the apple snail when builders drain swampland to put up buildings, the apple snails die out. then the snail kites have nothing to eat we must put a stop to putting buildings where endangered animals live

_____

_____

_____

_____

_____

_____

_____

_____

_____

_____

At Home: Invite the student to write a diary entry about a personal experience helping to protect or study wildlife.

© Macmillan/McGraw-Hill

Name_____

Rewrite each run-on sentence, adding the punctuation and conjunctions shown in parentheses.

1. The Florida manatee has been one of the most protected animals on earth it may now be in danger. (Add a comma and the conjunction *but*.)

_____

_____

2. The marine mammal is listed as endangered is protected by the federal Marine Mammal Act. (Add a comma and the conjunction *and*.)

_____

_____

3. Scientists with the Florida Fish and Wildlife Commission may reevaluate the protected status of the manatee the commission plans to act soon. (Add a semicolon.)

_____

_____

_____

4. Recreational boaters in Florida believe the manatee population has increased enough environmentalists disagree. (Add a semicolon, a comma and the conjunction *however*.)

_____

_____

_____

5. Manatee lovers admit that the populations have increased in some areas populations in other areas are low. (Add a comma and the conjunction *but*.)

_____

_____

_____

© Macmillan/McGraw-Hill

Name_____

> • A **run-on sentence** joins together two or more sentences that should be written separately.

Rewrite these run-on sentences using correct punctuation and capitalization.

1. the sea horse has two skeletons one is inside, and one is outside

   _____

   _____

2. the tail of the sea horse is very important it uses its tail to grip or hold on to things

   _____

   _____

3. this tiny animal can hang like a monkey it can swim in an upright position

   _____

   _____

4. the mother sea horse lays her eggs in the father's pouch the father cares for the eggs

   _____

   _____

5. sea horses are used to make medicine that means the species is at risk

   _____

   _____

6. black bears are carnivores eat very little meat live on grass fruits berries nuts.

   _____

   _____

Read the passage and look at each underlined section. Is there a mistake? If there is, how do you correct it? Circle the letter of your answer.

Most people think of school when they hear the word "education." But
(1)
traveling is an excellent way to learn. Each area of the country has its own
(2)
distinct animals and trees? Where else can you see a Florida manatee but in
Florida?

1. **A.** Change Most to most.
   B. Replace the period with an exclamation point.
   C. Replace the period with a question mark.
   D. No mistake

2. **A.** Change Each to each.
   B. Replace the question mark with an exclamation point.
   C. Replace the question mark with a period.
   D. No mistake

Read the passage below. How would you describe each group of underlined words? Circle the letter of your answer.

There are three levels of protection given to animals in danger of extinction.
The first level is the highest level: endangered. The second level has been
(3)
titled "threatened." Animals on the third level. are called "species of
(4)
special concern."

3. **A.** A complete sentence
   B. A sentence fragment missing a simple subject
   C. A sentence fragment missing a complete subject
   D. A sentence fragment missing a complete predicate subject

4. **A.** A complete sentence
   B. A sentence fragment missing a simple subject
   C. A sentence fragment missing a complete subject
   D. A sentence fragment missing a complete predicate

Read the passage. Circle the answer that describes each underlined sentence.

John loves and cares for his tropical fish, and often he adds to his
                        (5)
collection. John owns two Betta fish called Buddy and Freddy. John and
his sister, Sandy, own two of these colorful sea creatures, and they
                        (6)
often do research on how to care for them. There are many questions to
answer and ask. What kind of tank is best? What is the best kind of food?
It's a big responsibility caring for living things.

5. **A.** Simple sentence with compound subject
   B. Simple sentence with compound predicate
   C. Compound sentence with compound subject
   D. Compound sentence with compound predicate

6. **A.** Simple sentence with compound subject
   B. Simple sentence with compound predicate
   C. Compound sentence with compound subject
   D. Compound sentence with compound predicate

Read the passage and look at each underlined sentence. Is there a mistake? If there is, how do you correct it? Circle the letter of your answer.

John often looks to Sandy for help with Buddy and Freddy. While Sandy
was changing the water in the tank John watched her carefully. John
                        (7)
wanted to know the correct temperature of the water. Buddy and Freddy
        (8)
are going to stay happy and healthy.

7. **A.** Add a comma after *tank.*
   B. Add a comma and a conjunction after *tank.*
   C. Add a conjunction after *tank.*
   D. No mistake

8. **A.** Add a comma after *know.*
   B. Add a comma and a conjunction after *know.*
   C. Add a conjunction after *temperature.*
   D. No mistake

© Macmillan/McGraw-Hill

- A **noun** names a person, place, thing, or idea.
- A **common noun** names any person, place, thing, or idea.
- A **proper noun** names a particular person, place, thing, or idea and begins with a capital letter.

Read each sentence. Then underline each common noun once. Put brackets [ ] around each proper noun.

1. My cousin, Alex, plays football for a local team, the Broncos.

2. He and his friend, Jason, both go to Central High School here in town.

3. Besides playing sports, Alex and Jason also play bass in the orchestra.

4. The boys enjoy several subjects, including American History and English.

5. Their school has the leading debate team in all of Seminole County.

6. Ashley and Leroy, brother and sister, are captains of the debate team.

7. The students debate other teams from other parts of the state every third Wednesday.

8. Alex is thinking of joining the chess club, too, but he doesn't have much extra time.

9. He works at the Central City Public Library shelving books on Saturdays.

10. Between school, football, clubs, and work, Alex has to plan his days carefully.

11. Last month Alex and his family had a huge picnic in the park in the city.

12. Alex planned to write a letter to his friend Horatio who lives in Miami.

© Macmillan/McGraw-Hill

At Home: Have the student identify as many common and proper nouns as they can locate in a magazine or book.

How Tia Lola Came to Stay
Grade 6/Unit 2

33

Name_____

- Some proper nouns contain more than one word. Each important word begins with a capital letter.
- The name of a day, month, or holiday begins with a capital letter.

Identify all of the proper nouns in the following sentences. Rewrite each sentence, capitalizing all the proper nouns.

1. The broncos is a football team in our town of centerville.

   _____

   _____

2. mr. suarez is the coach for our rival football team, the panthers.

   _____

   _____

3. The broncos play on a field behind delaney creek boulevard, a main road.

   _____

   _____

4. Football is a popular sport in the state of florida.

   _____

   _____

5. The labor day kickoff party is enjoyed by all the citizens of centerville.

   _____

   _____

Write a proper noun for each of the following categories.

6. building _____

7. day of the week _____

8. month _____

9. holiday _____

10. country _____

At Home: Have the student write at least two more proper nouns for the categories above.

Name

> • Begin the greeting and closing of a business letter with a capital letter.
> • Use a colon after the greeting of a business letter. Use a comma after the closing.
> • Use a comma between the names of a city and a state.
> • Use a comma between the day and year in a date.

Proofread this business letter for errors in punctuation and capitalization. Make the necessary corrections.

144 East Arrowhead Drive

Charlotte North Carolina 28201

June 2 2005

The Carolina Lightnin'

P.O. Box 7252

Charlotte North Carolina 28207

dear Sir or Madam

    My family and I just moved here from Colorado. As soccer fans, we would like to receive the following information.

    We would like to have a schedule of Lightnin' home games. Also, we'd like to know the cost of tickets.

    Thank you for your assistance.

      sincerely yours

      Katrina Halbertstam

At Home: Have the student write a business letter asking for information.

How Tia Lola Came to Stay
Grade 6/Unit 2

35

Name_____

- A **common noun** names any person, place, thing, or idea, and does not begin with a capital letter unless it begins a sentence.
- Some proper nouns contain more than one word. Each important word begins with a capital letter. The name of a day, month, or holiday begins with a capital letter.

Proofread this business letter for errors in capitalization and punctuation. Underline any letters you think should be capitalized. Put brackets [ ] around any letters you think should not be capitalized. Make the necessary corrections in punctuation for a business letter.

978 river road

ramsey new jersey 07446

april 15 2005

The arizona cacti

P.O. Box 1234

chandler arizona 85224

dear sir or madam

    I have just begun school here in new jersey, but my Family used to live in arizona and utah. I would like to attend baseball camp during the Summer of 2005 with your organization. My Family will be traveling to arizona for the fourth of july, so the week of july 9 through july 15 would be best. Please let me know the cost of one Week of camp and any Equipment I might need to bring with me.

    Thank you for your assistance.

sincerely yours

Matthew Perricone

© Macmillan/McGraw-Hill

At Home: Have the student write a business letter to the sports team of their choosing, using correct punctuation and capitalization.

Name_____

Circle the letter of the correct form of capitalization for the underlined proper nouns. If the word or words is correctly capitalized, circle C for _no error_.

1. Isabel traveled to Knoxville, Tennessee, with her softball team, the <u>chattanooga wildcats</u>.

   a. Chattanooga wildcats

   b. Chattanooga Wildcats

   c. no error

2. All team members stayed at the Tyson Park Hotel on <u>beaumont avenue</u>.

   a. Beaumont Avenue

   b. Beaumont avenue

   c. no error

3. If Isabel and her team members win, they may travel to <u>england and ireland</u>.

   a. England and ireland

   b. England and Ireland

   c. no error

4. The tournament is scheduled for <u>monday, may 30, memorial day</u>.

   a. Monday, May 30, Memorial Day

   b. Monday, may 30, Memorial Day

   c. no error

5. Isabel took copies of _National Geographic_ to read on the bus trip.

   a. _national Geographic_

   b. _national geographic_

   c. no error

At Home: Have the student find examples of proper nouns in newspaper or magazine articles.

How Tía Lola Came to Stay **37**
Grade 6/Unit 2

Name_____

- A **common noun** names any person, place, thing, or idea.
- A **proper noun** names a particular person, place, thing, or idea.
- Some proper nouns may contain more than one word.
  Capitalize each important word.

**Read the following nouns. Decide whether each noun should be written
with a capital letter. Then write each noun under the correct picture.**

1. county historical
   society _____   _____

2. bijou theater _____   _____

3. lunch _____   _____

4. movie _____   _____

5. waldham
   university _____   _____

6. taxi _____   _____

7. friendship _____   _____

8. lenoir city
   state park _____   _____

9. assistant _____   _____

10. jackson,
    Mississippi _____   _____

© Macmillan/McGraw-Hill

At Home: Ask the student to find ten examples of proper
and common nouns in books or magazines.

Name_____

- A **singular noun** names one person, place, thing, or idea.
- A **plural noun** names more than one person, place, thing, or idea.
- Add -*s* to form the plural of most singular nouns.
- Add -*es* to form the plural of singular nouns that end in *s*, *sh*, *ch*, or *x*.

Read each sentence. Underline each singular noun. Put brackets [ ] around each plural noun.

1. Hector Menendez was happy to get a new telescope as one of his birthday gifts.

2. Hector enjoys gazing at the stars with his grandfather.

3. Mr. Menendez knows a lot about the planets and space.

4. He was a teacher for many years in local schools.

5. Hector has had serious thoughts about becoming an astronaut.

Write the plural form of each singular noun below.

6. planet _____

7. newspaper _____

8. brush _____

9. project _____

10. minute _____

11. shoe _____

12. branch _____

13. legend _____

14. mix _____

15. experience _____

© Macmillan/McGraw-Hill

At Home: Have the student list ten singular nouns and ten plural nouns seen around him or her.

The Night of the Pomegranate

39

Grade 6/Unit 2

Name_____

- Add -*es* to form the plural of singular nouns that end in *s*, *sh*, *ch*, or *x*.
- To form the plural of nouns ending in a consonant and *y*, change the *y* to *i* and add -*es*.
- To form the plural of nouns ending in a vowel and *y*, add -*s*.
- If a noun ends in *f*, sometimes add -*s*, or change the *f* to a *v* and add -*es*. Change *lf* to *v* and add -*es*.

Correct the misspellings of the plural nouns in these sentences.

1. Hector believes in his fantasys about becoming an astronaut.

_____

2. He plans to begin his studys to become a pilot soon.

_____

3. Yesterday, Hector got two boxs of books in the mail about space travel.

_____

4. There will be no delayes for Hector in his goal to reach outer space.

_____

5. Lots of girls and boyes at Hector's school share his dream.

_____

Write the plural form of each singular noun below.

6. roof _____
7. speech _____
8. community _____
9. glass _____
10. journey _____
11. self _____
12. flash _____

At Home: Ask the student to choose five of the nouns above and write two sentences for each.

© Macmillan/McGraw-Hill

Name _____

> • A comma tells the reader to pause between the words that it separates.
> • Use commas to separate three or more words in a series.
> • Do not use a comma after the last word in a series.

**Rewrite each sentence, inserting commas in the correct places.
One sentence needs no commas.**

1. Hector's favorite planets are Mars Venus Jupiter and Earth.

   _____

   _____

2. Hector gathered paints pencils paintbrushes and poster board for his project.

   _____

   _____

3. His project would show the scope the wonder and the beauty of the solar system.

   _____

   _____

4. Hector's mom brought him milk fruit nuts and cookies while he worked.

   _____

   _____

5. Hector ate only the milk and fruit.

   _____

   _____

At Home: Have the student write five sentences that contain items in a series, inserting commas in the correct places.

The Night of the Pomegranate
Grade 6/Unit 2

41

Name_____

- Add -*s* to form the plural of most singular nouns.
- Add -*es* to form the plural of singular nouns that end in *s*, *sh*, *ch*, or *x*.
- To form the plural of nouns ending in a consonant and *y*, change the *y* to *i* and add -*es*.
- To form the plural of nouns ending in a vowel and *y*, add -*s*.

Proofread this editorial for errors in spelling and puncutation. Put brackets [ ] around any misspellings of singular or plural nouns. Add commas in a series where needed.

Editorial from the *Sun City Sentinel*:

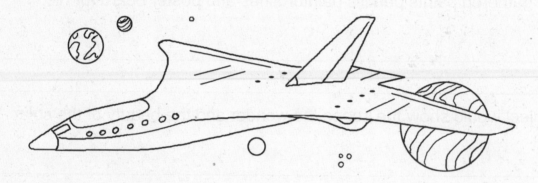

    This country spends far too much money on space travel. We have enough problem right here on Earth! We need to improve our road systems water systems and air quality. We need our communitys to band together to think of fixs for these problem. How many discoverys must astronauts make? Large quantitys of money spent on space exploration will not make Earth a better places to live! Let's get together—friendes enemys and all—no more fantasys about space!

At Home: Have the student write an editorial about space travel, using plurals and series commas correctly.

© Macmillan/McGraw-Hill

Complete the following sentences. Use the plural form of the noun in parentheses.

1. Hector has been collecting (rock) for many years.

   _____

2. He keeps them in (box) in the attic.

   _____

3. He recently found a rare one between two (blade) of grass.

   _____

4. He always looks under (bush) for special finds.

   _____

5. Hector has a special pair of (glass) he wears in the sun.

   _____

6. He sometimes brings (berry) to eat on his rock-hunting trips.

   _____

7. There are several different (approach) to rock collecting.

   _____

8. Some people have elaborate (ceremony) before they begin.

   _____

9. Hector thinks these are sturdy (shelf).

   _____

10. He just makes a few (sandwich) and heads out the door.

    _____

11. Sunlight shone through the (leaf) on the trees.

    _____

12. (bunch) of wild grapes grew on the vines.

    _____

At Home: Ask the student to open a book or magazine and find ten singular and ten plural nouns.

Name_____

- A **plural noun** names more than one person, place, thing, or idea.
- Add -s to form the plural of most singular nouns.
- Add -es to form the plural of singular nouns that end in s, sh, ch, or x.
- To form the plural of nouns ending in a consonant and y, change y to i and add -es.
- To form the plural of nouns ending in a vowel and y, add -s.

Mechanics

- Use commas to separate three or more words in a series.
- Do not use a comma after the last word in a series.

Work with a partner. One partner reads a sentence, changing the singular nouns to plural nouns. The other partner writes the sentence correctly, using commas where they are needed. Exchange papers to proofread each other's sentences.

1. Hector's grandfather encourages him to have tie to the local science museum.

_____

_____

2. Hector knows he must be strong brave and stubborn to become an astronaut.

_____

_____

3. He has spent many evenings studying math physics and chemistry.

_____

_____

4. Hector's parents are both attorney, with big office important title and grand case.

_____

_____

At Home: Ask the student to write a short paragraph including singular and plural nouns explaining their plans for the future.

Name_____

- To form the plural of most nouns ending in *f* or *fe*, add *-s*.
- For others, change the *f* to *v* and add *-es*.

Write the plural form of each singular noun below.

1. half _____
2. wolf _____
3. loaf _____
4. dwarf _____
5. life _____
6. wife _____
7. puff _____
8. knife _____
9. spoof _____

Rewrite these sentences using the correct plural form.

10. Rosita is one of many executive cheves at the restaurant.

_____

_____

11. Rosita owns several expensive knifes, which she uses in her work.

_____

_____

12. She keeps her pots and pans on the shelfs above the stove.

_____

_____

© Macmillan/McGraw-Hill

At Home: Have the student choose five of the plural nouns above and use them in a sentence.

Name_____

- To form the plural of nouns that end with a vowel and *o*, add *-s*.
- To form the plural of nouns that end with a consonant and *o*, add *-s* or *-es*.
- Some nouns have special plural forms.
- A few nouns have the same singular and plural forms.

Write the plural form of each singular noun below.

1. mouse   _____

2. rodeo   _____

3. potato   _____

4. ox   _____

5. concerto   _____

6. silo   _____

7. wolf   _____

8. self   _____

9. child   _____

10. moose   _____

11. headquarters   _____

12. knife   _____

13. ratio   _____

14. mix   _____

15. goose   _____

At Home: Have the student write a paragraph in which he or she uses five of the nouns above in plural form.

- To form the plural of most nouns ending in *f* or *fe*, add *-s*.
- For other nouns, change the *f* to *v* and add *-es*.
- To form the plural of nouns that end with a vowel and *o*, add *-s*.
- To form the plural of nouns that end with a consonant and *o*, add *-s* or *-es*.
- Some nouns have special plural forms that must be memorized.
- A few nouns have the same singular and plural forms.

Read each sentence. If the sentence contains an incorrect plural form, rewrite it using the correct plural form. If the sentence is correct, write C on the line.

1. Alicia's father took photoes of the hurricane damage. _____

2. There were knifes all over the kitchen floor after the storm. _____

3. The children helped to pick up fallen branches in the yard. _____

4. Some familys had nowhere to live. _____

5. The local grocery store donated many boxs of food. _____

6. Everybody ate lots of potatos the week after the storm. _____

7. The roofs came off completely on several houses. _____

8. Lots of people became heros overnight. _____

9. They delivered loafs of bread and gallons of milk to hungry people.

   _____

10. Men and womans all over the town handed out ice and water.

    _____

At Home: Have the student make flash cards with the singular spelling on the front and the plural spelling on the back.

Zoo Story • Grade 6/Unit 2 47

Name_____

- To form the plural of most nouns ending in *f* or *fe*, add *-s*.
- For other nouns, change the *f* to *v* and add *-es*.
- To form the plural of nouns that end with a vowel and *o*, add *-s*.
- To form the plural of nouns that end with a consonant and *o*, add *-s* or *-es*.
- Some nouns have special plural forms that must be memorized.
- A few nouns have the same singular and plural forms.

Proofread this passage. Then rewrite the passage using the correct plural form. Correct any mistakes in capitalization or punctuation.

   since I live in florida, I have a lot of personal experience with hurricanes. This summer, four hurricanes hit the state of florida my parents made sure we had plenty of canned food water and diapers for the baby batterys were in short supply at the store, and all the familys on my street rushed out to buy the few battery-powered radioes left on the store shelfs we were safe and dry in our house we had three loafs of bread and lots of peanut butter

_____

_____

_____

_____

_____

_____

_____

_____

At Home: Invite the student to write a short paragraph about a rain- or snowstorm, using at least three plural nouns in their writing.

Name_____

Put a circle around the noun or nouns that are spelled correctly in each row.

1. mouses   wolves   womens
2. bluffs   wifes   zooes
3. radioes   deers   moose
4. geese   studioes   lifes
5. siloes   oxen   mans

**Rewrite the nouns from the lists above that are not spelled correctly.
Then use each noun in a sentence.**

6. _____

_____

7. _____

_____

8. _____

_____

9. _____

_____

10. _____

_____

11. _____

_____

12. _____

_____

13. _____

_____

14. _____

_____

15. _____

_____

At Home: Ask the student to write a short paragraph on the
subject of mice, or deer, using the correct plural forms of
these nouns.

Name_____

> - To form the plural of most nouns ending in *f* or *fe*, add -*s*.
> - For other nouns, change the *f* to *v* and add -*es*.
> - To form the plural of nouns that end with a vowel and *o*, add -*s*.
> - To form the plural of nouns that end with a consonant and *o*, add -*s* or -*es*.
> - Some nouns have special plural forms that must be memorized.
> - A few nouns have the same singular and plural forms.

Correct the errors in plural nouns in each sentence. Write the sentence with the correct capital letters.

1. Some animals were as small as gooses. Some animals were as large as oxes.

   _____

   _____

2. When hurricanes hit zooes, all animals, great and small, suffer.

   _____

   _____

3. The force of the wind blew the rooves off the animal cagess.

   _____

   _____

4. Everybody at zoo headquarteres was very worried.

   _____

   _____

5. They listened on their radioes for news about the hurricane.

   _____

   _____

At Home: Ask the student to write a brief paragraph in which he or she uses five of the words above in plural form.

Name_____

> • A **possessive noun** is a noun that shows who or what owns or has something.
> • Form a **singular possessive noun** by adding an apostrophe (') and -s to a singular noun.

Circle the possessive noun or nouns in each sentence. Then write what the possessive noun owns or has.

1. The fairy tale was about an old king's daughter.

_____

2. The girl's mother was very protective of her.

_____

3. The daughter's name was Aurora.

_____

4. Aurora's life was very different from yours or mine.

_____

5. Her father's riches could not protect her.

_____

6. Her mother's love could not save her.

_____

7. Only Aurora's fairy godmother could help her.

_____

8. The old woman's skill with casting a spell was well known.

_____

9. The king's knowledge of it saved Aurora from an eternity of sleep.

_____

10. The fairy tale's ending is well known.

_____

At Home: Have the student shorten groups of words by using singular possessive nouns: the shoe of the girl; the skill of the boy.

Rumpelstiltskin's Daughter
Grade 6/Unit 2
51

Name_____

- A **plural possessive** noun is a plural noun that shows ownership.
- To form the possessive of a plural noun that ends in -*s*, add an apostrophe.
- To form the possessive of a plural noun that does not end in -*s*, add an apostrophe and -*s*.

Write the plural possessive for each of the singular possessive nouns below.

1. writer's _____

2. boss's _____

3. story's _____

4. farmer's _____

5. man's _____

6. husband's _____

7. villager's _____

8. daughter's _____

9. father's _____

10. mother's _____

11. buffalo's _____

12. child's _____

13. thief's _____

14. woman's _____

15. moose's _____

16. mouse's _____

17. wolf's _____

18. zoo's _____

19. ox's _____

20. century's _____

At Home: Have the student choose five of the nouns listed above and write sentences for plural possessive forms.

- Add -s to most nouns to form the plural. Do not use an apostrophe.
- Add an apostrophe and -s to a singular noun to make it possessive.
- Add an apostrophe to make most plural nouns possessive. Add 's to plural nouns that do not end in -s.

Label the following nouns as *S* for singular, *SP* for singular possessive, *P* for plural, or *PP* for plural possessive.

1. city's _____
2. boat _____
3. Douglas _____
4. cats _____
5. Smiths' _____
6. rodeo's _____
7. painters _____
8. writers' _____
9. witness's _____
10. actors' _____
11. bicycle _____
12. boss _____
13. dogs _____
14. actresses' _____
15. Tim's _____

On the line, write the possessive form of each word in parentheses.

16. All of the (village) citizens were worried about Aurora.

_____

17. The (farmer) harvest was going to be a good one this year.

_____

18. The (story) ending was always a surprise. _____

19. Aurora's (father) advisers were deep in thought. _____

20. The (hero) arrival on the scene was expected. _____

© Macmillan/McGraw-Hill

At Home: Have the student choose five of the nouns in the first exercise above and write the other three forms for each.

Rumpelstiltskin's Daughter **53**
Grade 6/Unit 2

Name_____

- Add *-s* to most nouns to form the plural. Do not use an apostrophe.
- Add an apostrophe and *-s* to a singular noun to make it possessive.
- Add an apostrophe to make most plural nouns possessive. Add *'s* to plural nouns that do not end in *-s*.

Proofread this persuasive essay. Then rewrite the essay using the correct posssessive or plural form of the nouns. Add apostrophes and -s where needed to form possessive nouns. Correct any mistakes in capitalization or punctuation.

It is many peoples opinion that fairy tale's are too violent for childrens. I do not agree with this position. My grandparents' enjoyed reading aloud classic stories to my sister's and me. My sisters memorys of these read aloud time's are all wonderful, they assure me. As for me, Red Riding Hoods demise at the wolves hands did not scare me at all. I could not wait to hear what happened to Hansel and Gretel after they got fat enough! A childs delight should not be measured in such black and white terms.

At Home: Invite the student to write a short paragraph about a shared family tradition.

Name _____

Rewrite the following groups of words in possessive form.

1. the sounds of the village _____

2. the generosity of the elders _____

3. the hands of the thief _____

4. the scene of the movie _____

5. the peaks of the mountains _____

6. the cries of the children _____

7. the history of Spain _____

8. the sisters of Alex _____

9. the rivers of the South _____

10. the property of the villagers _____

11. the voice of the people _____

12. the legs of the oxen _____

13. the problems of society _____

14. the traditions of the families _____

15. the bite of the snake _____

16. the feathers of the birds _____

17. the paw of the lion _____

18. the roles of the actresses _____

19. the eyes of the tiger _____

20. the laughter of the girls _____

At Home: Ask the student to put together the "ideal" person by taking characteristics from various famous people.

Name_____

- A **possessive noun** is a noun that shows who or what owns or has something.
- Form a singular possessive noun by adding an apostrophe (') and -s to a singular noun.
- To form the possessive of a plural noun that ends in -s, add an apostrophe.
- To form the possessive of a plural noun that does not end in -s, add an apostrophe and -s.

Mechanics

- Add -s to most nouns to form the plural. Do not use an apostrophe.

Read each sentence aloud. Then rewrite the sentence using the correct singular or plural possessive noun. Place apostrophes in the correct places.

1. A young persons life in a fairy tale is usually one of danger and mystery.

_____

_____

2. Auroras story, like that of Cinderella, is told in many cultures.

_____

_____

3. *Sleeping Beauty* is Tashas favorite tale.

_____

4. The godmothers care of young Aurora was wonderful to read about.

_____

_____

5. Peoples fascination with fairy tales seems to be unending.

_____

_____

At Home: Ask the student to write five sentences about their favorite fairy tale, using possessives in each sentence.

© Macmillan/McGraw-Hill

Name_____

- An **appositive** is a word or group of words that follows a noun and identifies or explains the noun.
- Commas are used to set off most appositives from the rest of the sentence.

Read each sentence. If the sentence contains an appositive, write *A* on the line and circle the appositive word or phrase. If the sentence does not contain an appositive, write *N*.

1. The Great Serum Race began in Nome, a city in Alaska. _____

2. The city had several cases of diphtheria, a fast-spreading disease. _____

3. In 1925, Nome had a population of about 1,400 people. _____

4. The cure for diphtheria, antitoxin serum, was not available. _____

5. The nearest supply was in Anchorage, 1,000 miles away. _____

6. Bill Shannon, the first musher to carry the serum, left Anchorage on January 27. _____

7. Bill had a team of nine malamutes. _____

8. Togo, a proven leader, waited anxiously to begin his part of the race. _____

9. Togo's leader was Leonhard, the famed Norwegian musher. _____

10. Balto, another famous lead dog, finally finished the race and delivered the serum. _____

At Home: Have the student look through a newspaper or magazine and locate three appositives or appositive phrases.

Name_____

> • You can use an appositive to combine two short sentences in one.

Read each pair of sentences. Then combine them using an appositive word or phrase. Be sure to write the new sentence using a comma or commas to set off the appositive.

1. The serum was located in Anchorage. Anchorage is a city in southern Alaska.

_____

_____

2. Alfred John heard the roar of the steam engine. He was a five-year-old Athabaskan Indian.

_____

_____

3. Alfred wore his warmest shoes. They were caribou legskin boots.

_____

_____

4. Bill's dogsled team raced toward Tolovana. Tolovana was the first relay stop some fifty-two miles away.

_____

_____

5. Bill enjoyed his regular job. His regular job was transporting mail and freight with his dog team.

_____

_____

At Home: Have the students write three sentences containing appositives about places they visited and the people who lived in those places.

© Macmillan/McGraw-Hill

- Use commas to set off most appositives from the rest of the sentence.

Add commas where they are needed to set off appositives in the following sentences.

1. Leonhard wore his warmest clothing a squirrel skin parka, sealskin pants, and reindeer mukluks.

2. He was going to intercept the serum at Nulato a village halfway between Nome and Nenana.

3. Dog teams always wore bells a warning to pedestrians as they ran through town.

4. Togo led the team down Front Street the town's main road.

5. Edgar Kalland a twenty-year-old Athabaskan Indian mail driver waited anxiously.

6. He waited outside the Tolovana Roadhouse a favorite rest stop for dog-sled teams.

7. Edgar soon took off for Manly Hot Springs a thirty-one-mile trip to the next relay point.

8. The dogs had to wade through slush a dangerously wet snow that was caused by a crack in the ice.

9. Musher Charlie Evans faced the coldest temperatures sixty-four degrees below zero.

10. Balto a true hero finally saved the day.

At Home: Have the student write five sentences that contain appositives.

The Great Serum Race
Grade 6/Unit 2

59

Name_____

- An **appositive** is a word or group of words that follows a noun and identifies or explains the noun.
- Commas are used to set off most appositives from the rest of the sentence.
- You can use an appositive to combine two short sentences.

Proofread this persuasive essay. Then rewrite the essay using appositives to combine sentences. Add any necessary commas. Correct any mistakes in capitalization or punctuation.

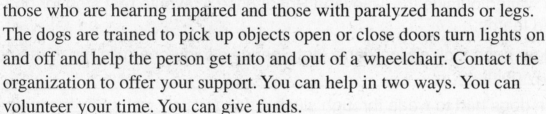

many dogs work hard every day. These Dogs are called service dogs. Our town has a program to train these animals. The program is called PAWS. PAWS dogs help not only people who are blind, but also those who are hearing impaired and those with paralyzed hands or legs. The dogs are trained to pick up objects open or close doors turn lights on and off and help the person get into and out of a wheelchair. Contact the organization to offer your support. You can help in two ways. You can volunteer your time. You can give funds.

_____

_____

_____

_____

_____

_____

_____

_____

 At Home: Invite the student to write a persuasive essay urging others to support a worthy cause.

Rewrite the following sentences. Underline the appositive word or phrase, adding commas where they are needed.

1. Alaska the home of the great Iditarod Race is a beautiful state.

2. On the west, it is bordered by the Bering Sea an immense expanse of water.

3. Canada a very large country shares Alaska's border.

4. Mount Denali also known as Mount McKinley is located in Alaska.

5. Denali Athabaskan for "The Great One" is over twenty thousand feet high.

Use appositives to combine each pair of sentences. Write the sentences on the line. Be sure to place the commas correctly.

6. Juneau is a large city in southeastern Alaska. Juneau is the capital of Alaska.

   _____

   _____

7. Ketchikan is famous for its fishing industry. Ketchikan is located near the Canadian border.

   _____

   _____

8. Noatak and Yukon Charley are beautiful national preserves. Noatak and Yukon Charley are located in Alaska.

   _____

   _____

9. Mount Denali is located in Denali National Park. Mount Denali is the highest point in North America.

   _____

   _____

10. The Yukon lies to the east of Alaska. The Yukon is part of Canada.

    _____

    _____

At Home: Ask the student to write a paragraph about a city that interests him or her.

- An **appositive** is a word or group of words that follows a noun and identifies or explains the noun. You can use an appositive to combine two short sentences into one.

Mechanics

- Use commas to set off most appositives from the rest of the sentence.

Use the groups of words below as appositives to write four sentences about a mountain you would like to climb. (You may make up some "make-believe" nouns, if you wish.) Be sure to place commas correctly.

1. a place of rare beauty

_____

_____

2. a mountain over twenty thousand feet high

_____

_____

3. also known as Mount McKinley

_____

_____

4. extreme cold and gale-force winds

_____

_____

At Home: Ask the student to write three sentences containing appositives about a challenge he or she would like to take on.

© Macmillan/McGraw-Hill

Read each passage and look at each underlined section. Is there a mistake? If there is, how do you correct it? Circle the letter of your answer.

<u>Miguel and Juanita moved from new york city to Vermont.</u> Tía Lola soon
(1)
came to live with them. <u>In june, when school let out, Miguel started practicing</u>
(2)
baseball. <u>When their neighbor, Colonel Charlebois, came to visit, Miguel felt
sure something would go wrong.</u>   (3)

1. **A.** Change new york city to New York city.
   B. Change Vermont to vermont.
   C. Change new york city to New York City.
   D. No mistake

2. **A.** Change In to in.
   B. Change school to School.
   C. Change june to June.
   D. No mistake

3. **A.** Change When to when.
   B. Change Colonel Charlebois to colonel Charlebois.
   C. Change neighbor to Neighbor.
   D. No mistake

<u>Some familys don't enjoy star-gazing.</u>   <u>But Louis family is not one of these.</u>
(4)   (5)

The Hernandez family has a high-powered telescope. Every member of the family, even little Juanita, knows the names of the planets and even some of their moons. They are solar-system enthusiasts.

4. **A.** Change familys to families.
   B. Change familys to family's.
   C. Change familys to familys'.
   D. No mistake

5. **A.** Change Louis to Louises.
   B. Change Louis to Louises'.
   C. Change Louis to Louis's.
   D. No mistake

© Macmillan/McGraw-Hill

Name_____

Read each passage and look at each underlined section. Is there a mistake? If there is, how do you correct it? Circle the letter of your answer.

My brother thinks that people who climb mountains like Denali are heros. I
(6)
agree with him. I look at all the roofes in my town, and even they seem to high
(7)
too climb. My personal belief is that people should stay on the ground.
(8)

6. **A.** Change Denali to denali.   8. **A.** Change My to my.

   B. Change brother to brother's.   **B.** Change beliefs to believes.

   C. Change heros to heroes.   **C.** Change beliefs to belief's.

   D. No mistake   **D.** No mistake

7. **A.** Change roofes to rooves'.

   B. Change roofes to roof's.

   C. Change roofes to roofs.

   D. No mistake

Sophia likes to talk about her grandparents home in Alaska. The girls
(9)   (10)
relatives lived in the city of Kodiak on Kodiak Island. This island is in the
southernmost part of Alaska.

9. **A.** Change grandparents to grandparents'.

   B. Change grandparents to Grandparents.

   C. Change Sophia to Sophia's.

   D. No mistake

10. **A.** Change girls to girles.

   B. Change girls to girls'.

   C. Change girls to girl's.

   D. No mistake

Name_____

> • An **action verb** is a word that expresses action. It tells what the subject does or did.
> • A **direct object** is a noun or pronoun that receives the action of the verb. It answers the question *what*? or *whom*? after the verb.

Underline the action verbs and circle the direct objects in the following sentences.

1. Jose buys roses.

2. Jose learns many facts.

3. His grandfather showed him the beautiful rose bushes.

4. Jose uses his nose.

5. One of his brothers got a new rose bush.

6. He planted the bush in the front yard.

7. Jose rides his bike every day.

8. His grandfather cuts the roses.

9. Jose plays the trumpet.

10. He performs all kinds of music.

11. Jose watches music concerts on television every Saturday.

12. Jose likes his teachers.

At Home: Identify action verbs and direct objects in a magazine or newspaper article.

- An **indirect object** is a noun or pronoun in the predicate that answers the question *to whom?* or *for whom?* or *to what?* or *for what?* after an action verb.

Underline each action verb once and each direct object twice. Put brackets [ ] around each indirect object.

1. Mr. Wagner gave Jose some lessons.

2. Mrs. Wagner baked everybody cookies.

3. Jose read his sister a story.

4. His sister sang Jose a song.

5. Jose's grandfather gave him some good advice.

6. Jose sent his mother a birthday card.

7. She gave him her thanks.

8. Mr. Wagner bought his daughter a violin.

9. She showed us her violin.

10. Jose handed Mrs. Wagner a red rose.

11. Jose played his grandfather music.

12. Schools give music students excellent opportunities.

© Macmillan/McGraw-Hill

At Home: Write a paragraph about a flower. Underline each action verb once and each direct object twice.

Name_____

- A verb must agree with its subject.
- Add -s to most verbs if the subject is singular. Do not add -s if the subject is plural or *I* or *you*.

Rewrite each sentence below, making the correct choices from the words in parentheses so that subjects and their verbs agree.

1. Jose (want, wants) to learn about growing roses.

   _____

2. You (shop, shops) for new rose bushes each year in May.

   _____

3. Jose (know, knows) that taking care of roses is a lot of work.

   _____

4. His grandparents (tell, tells) Jose all about different kinds of roses.

   _____

5. I (give, gives) Jose a beautiful pink rose.

   _____

6. Jose (offer, offers) his grandfather a hand.

   _____

7. Jose (ask, asks) his grandfather a question.

   _____

8. Jose (buy, buys) his grandmother some roses.

   _____

9. The flowers (make, makes) the neighbor sneeze.

   _____

10. Jose's grandfather (plant, plants) rose bushes every year.

    _____

© Macmillan/McGraw-Hill

At Home: In the sentences above, draw an arrow from each subject to the verb with which it agrees.

Name_____

- An **action verb** is a word that expresses action. It tells what the subject does or did.
- A **direct object** is a noun or pronoun that receives the action of the verb. It answers the question *what*? or *whom*? after the verb.
- An **indirect object** is a noun or pronoun in the predicate that answers *to whom*? or *for whom*? or *to what*? after an action verb. An indirect always comes before a direct object.

Rewrite the character sketch below correcting any mistakes made with verbs that do not agree with their subjects.

Jose's grandfather are always telling him stories about old New Mexico. Popi are a small man, thin and wiry. He has unusually large hands, though, the fingers thick and blunt. He wear heavy black glasses with thick plastic lenses. His eyes is pale brown, almost yellow-gold. Popi come from Mexico, and although his English seem perfect, he speak with a faint accent, almost as if he are singing. Popi often sing Jose songs from Mexico.

_____
_____
_____
_____
_____
_____
_____
_____
_____
_____

© Macmillan/McGraw-Hill

At Home: Write a character sketch of someone you know, using at least one indirect object.

Name_____

Read each sentence. Write whether the underlined word is a direct object, an indirect object, or an action verb.

1. Jose told <u>Popi</u> a story.

2. Popi <u>asked</u> Jose about the new roses.

3. Jose read the <u>book</u> out loud.

4. Popi played Jose a new <u>song</u>.

5. Jose <u>bought</u> his mom a rose.

6. He bought <u>Popi</u> a book.

7. Jose <u>told</u> Popi a joke.

8. Popi asked Jose a <u>question</u>.

9. Jose plays his <u>trumpet</u> every evening.

10. Jose's teacher gave the <u>class</u> homework.

Name_____

- An **action verb** is a word that expresses action. It tells what the subject does or did.
- A **direct object** is a noun or pronoun that receives the action of the verb. It answers the question *what*? or *whom*? after the verb.
- An **indirect object** is a noun or pronoun in the predicate that answers the question *to whom*? or *for whom*? or *to what*? or *for what*? after an action verb. An indirect object always comes before a direct object.

Mechanics

- Use commas to separate three or more words in a series.
- Do not use a comma after the last word in a series.

Look at the picture. Rewrite each sentence, using the picture to help describe it. Add the sentence part or punctuation shown in parentheses.

1. Popi gave a rose. (Add an indirect object.)

   _____

2. Jose will cut. (Add a direct object.)

   _____

3. Popi will tell how to grow roses. (Add an indirect object.)

   _____

4. Popi's garden has roses daisies and tulips. (Add punctuation.)

   _____

- A verb in the **present tense** tells what happens now.
- In the present tense, you must have **subject-verb agreement.** Add -*s* to most verbs if the subject is singular. Do not add -*s* if the subject is plural or *I* or *you*.

Rewrite each sentence below, using the correct verb in parentheses.

1. Eva (open, opens) her notebook and (begin, begins) to write.

_____

2. Her teacher (tell, tells) her to write what she (know, knows).

_____

3. Eva (sit, sits) on her stoop and (look, looks) out over 90th Street.

_____

_____

4. I (think, thinks) Eva may be bored.

_____

5. You (know, knows) she has to stay busy.

_____

6. The teacher (tell, tells) the students to speak loudly.

_____

7. When she writes on her stoop, Eva's words (come, comes) easily.

_____

_____

8. Most of the students (do, does) not like to write.

_____

At Home: Write a paragraph about a journal you would like to keep. Make sure that each verb agrees with the subject.

Name_____

- A verb in the **past tense** tells about an action that already happened.
- Add *-ed* to most verbs to show past tense.
- A verb in the **future tense** tells about an action that is going to happen.
- To write about the future, use the special verb *will*.

Write the verb in parentheses in the past tense.

1. Eva (want) something exciting to happen on her street.

   _____

2. A whole week (pass) with nothing for her to do.

   _____

3. Eva's friend (whisper) to her that someone was coming to visit.

   _____

4. Eva (dress) up in her best outfit.

   _____

5. Her friend (warn) Eva not to get too excited.

   _____

6. Eva (hope) that something would happen soon.

   _____

Change the following verbs into the future tense.

7. like _____

8. enjoy _____

9. pick _____

10. make _____

11. remove _____

12. build _____

At Home: Write sentences for the six verbs in the future tense above.

Name_____

- Use quotation marks before and after the words of a direct quotation.
- Use a comma before a quotation when the speaker's name comes first.
- Use a comma, a question mark, or an exclamation point to end the quotation when the speaker's name comes last.

Proofread each sentence. Then rewrite the sentence using the correct punctuation for dialogue.

1. Do you think anything will happen today asked Eva

_____

_____

2. Kevin asked Will you be coming to the play tonight, Eva

_____

_____

3. I'd love to come said Eva

_____

4. Kevin said I'll pick you up at six o'clock

_____

5. Take me, too yelled Sarah

_____

6. Write about what you know said Mrs. DeMarco

_____

7. Nothing ever happens on this street yelled Eva

_____

8. Are you all right asked Eva

_____

At Home: Write a dialogue you might have with a friend. Remember to use correct punctuation.

Nothing Ever Happens on 90th Street • **Grade 6/Unit 3**

73

- A verb in the **present tense** tells what happens now.
- In the present tense, you must have **subject-verb agreement.** Add -*s* to most verbs if the subject is singular. Do not add -*s* if the subject is plural or *I* or *you*.
- A verb in the **past tense** tells about an action that already happened.
- Add -*ed* to most verbs to show past tense.
- A verb in the **future tense** tells about an action that is going to happen.
- To write about the future, use the special verb *will*.

The writer of this dialogue did not proofread for mistakes. Put brackets [ ] around any incorrect verb tenses. Rewrite the dialogue correcting verb forms and adding correct punctuation.

Juliet and Romeo were sitting at the library table.

Juliet said Don't look at my journal, Romeo

I was not looking cry Romeo

Yes, you were I sees you cry Juliet

Romeo whispers keeps your voice down

I'm only trying to puts my thoughts and feelings into writing whisper Juliet

Go right ahead say Romeo

Juliet replied Thank you. I do just that

_____

_____

_____

_____

_____

_____

_____

_____

 At Home: Write a dialogue in which you have a disagreement with a friend. Use correct punctuation and verb tenses.

Circle the letter of the choice that corrects each numbered sentence. If there is no error in the sentence, circle *c* for *correct*.

1. Last night, Eva attend the play with Kevin.

   a. Last night, Eva attends the play with Kevin.

   b. Last night, Eva attended the play with Kevin.

   c. correct

2. Tomorrow she will attend the ballet with her father.

   a. Tomorrow she attended the ballet with her father.

   b. Tomorrow she attend the ballet with her father.

   c. correct

3. Eva laugh at the play's silly plot.

   a. Eva laughed at the play's silly plot.

   b. Eva laughing at the play's silly plot.

   c. correct

4. Yesterday Eva's parents watch the same play.

   a. Yesterday Eva's parents watches the same play.

   b. Yesterday Eva's parents watched the same play.

   c. correct

5. By the end of the play, everyone guess who had committed the crime.

   a. By the end of the play, everyone guessed who had committed the crime.

   b. By the end of the play, everyone guessing who had committed the crime.

   c. correct

6. Eva write a review of the play in her notebook.

   a. Eva writes a review of the play in her notebook.

   b. Eva wrote a review of the play in her notebook.

   c. correct

© Macmillan/McGraw-Hill

Name_____

- In the present tense, you must have **subject-verb agreement.** Add -*s* to most verbs if the subject is singular. Do not add -*s* if the subject is plural or *I* or *you*.
- Add -*ed* to most verbs to show past tense.
- To write about the future, use the special verb *will*.

Mechanics

- If a verbs ends in *s*, *ch*, *sh*, *x*, or *z*, add -*es* in the present with a singular subject.
- If a verb ends with a consonant and *y*, change *y* to *i* and add -*es* for present or -*ed* for past.
- If a verb ends with *e*, drop the *e* and add -*ed* for the past.
- If a verb ends with one vowel and one consonant, double the consonant before adding -*ed* for the past.

Correct the spelling of the verbs and their tenses in the sentences below.

1. The students study all day yesterday.

   _____

2. Annette mix colors for her painting this morning.

   _____

3. Last week, Kevin promise to take Eva to the play.

   _____

4. Eva and Kevin clap their hands after the actors took a bow.

   _____

   _____

5. Eva change into her new outfit before Kevin came over.

   _____

   _____

Name _____

- A **verb phrase** is made up of a main verb and one or more helping verbs. A **helping verb** helps the main verb show an action or make a statement.
- Common helping verbs are *am, are, is, was, were, have, has, had, do, does, did, be, being, been, will, shall, can, could, would, should, might, must.*

Write the verb phrases in the following sentences.

1. Anthony is helping his cousin with his business. _____

2. His cousin has started a solar-energy firm. _____

3. Solar energy will help the economy. _____

4. Anthony has been shown the data. _____

5. Anthony will learn all about solar energy. _____

6. He has seen it in many homes. _____

7. Usually, the sun is shining where Anthony lives. _____

8. Anthony's cousin will teach him a lot. _____

9. He had asked Anthony about the job. _____

10. Anthony must remember many facts. _____

11. Anthony had always wanted a job like this. _____

12. Anthony and his cousin will travel to work together. _____

At Home: Choose five of the helping verbs listed in the box above and use them to write sentences.

- Main and helping verbs form different verb tenses.

Tense	Example
Present perfect	I have walked
Past perfect	I had walked
Present progressive	I am walking
Past progressive	I was walking
Future progressive	I will be walking

A. **Name the tense of each of the following verbs.**

1. am sitting _____

2. have seen _____

3. ride _____

4. will be sleeping _____

5. had studied _____

6. am helping _____

B. **Write the form shown in parentheses for the verb in each sentence.**

7. I work. (present progressive)

_____

8. We worked here before. (past perfect)

_____

9. We will work here for a while. (future progressive)

_____

10. I will work for Anthony's cousin this summer. (past progressive)

_____

11. I am working hard. (present perfect)

_____

12. I wait. (future progressive)

_____

© Macmillan/McGraw-Hill

At Home: Choose four of the verbs in Part A above and write sentences for them.

Name_____

- A contraction is a shortened form of two words.
- A contraction can be made by combining a verb with the word *not*.
- An apostrophe (') shows that the letter *o* has been left out.

These contractions are formed from helping verbs. In each case, the apostrophe replaces the letter o in not.

isn't = is not

won't = will not

doesn't = does not

couldn't = could not

mustn't = must not

Write the contractions for the following helping verbs and *not*.

1. has not   _____

2. were not   _____

3. was not   _____

4. have not   _____

5. are not   _____

Write the correct contraction of the helping verb and *not* on the line. Be sure to put the apostrophe in the correct place.

6. Anthony _____ going to work on Saturday.

7. He _____ miss band practice this week.

8. His band leader _____ happy with his trombone playing.

9. Anthony _____ seem to play the notes correctly.

10. He _____ want to disappoint his leader.

At Home: Write three sentences about a skill you have had difficulty mastering. Use a contraction in each of the sentences.

- A **verb phrase** is made up of a main verb and one or more helping verbs. A **helping verb** helps the main verb show an action or make a statement.
- Common helping verbs are *am, are, is, was, were, have, has, had, do, does, did, be, being, been, will, shall, can, could, would, should, might, must*.

The writer of this point of view essay did not proofread for mistakes. Rewrite the essay correcting any mistakes made in verb tense. Then underline the verb phrases.

It is my opinion that people in this city should be ride bicycles instead of driving cars. You can safely riding a bike to many destinations. I myself riding mine to the grocery store the library and the post office. I have always think that jump into a car for no good reason are a big waste of gas. If you would took a trip to Beijing Tokyo or Amsterdam, you would saw hundreds of people happily ride their bikes to work and school. We can done it here, too.

_____

_____

_____

_____

_____

_____

_____

_____

_____

_____

At Home: Write a short paragraph about a way to save energy, using at least three helping verbs in your writing.

Name_____

Rewrite each underlined verb in the tense given in parentheses.

1. She <u>chops</u> some wood before leaving for school. (past perfect)

_____

_____

2. He <u>asks</u> his cousin for advice on building a windmill. (past)

_____

_____

3. They <u>became</u> very skilled at putting in solar-energy panels. (present perfect)

_____

_____

4. I <u>heard</u> that Anthony is thinking of becoming an engineer. (past perfect)

_____

5. I <u>help</u> Anthony tomorrow morning. (future progressive)

_____

6. She <u>ask</u> the teacher for advice. (present)

_____

7. The writers <u>construct</u> their stories from real events. (past)

_____

_____

8. By the time we were adults, I <u>become</u> a scientist. (past perfect)

_____

_____

9. I will <u>wait</u> for Anthony for a long time. (future progressive)

_____

10. I <u>waited</u> for help on the solar-energy project. (past progressive)

_____

At Home: Write a short paragraph on the subject of a future career, using the future and future progressive tenses.

- A **verb phrase** is made up of a main verb and one or more helping verbs. A **helping verb** helps the main verb show an action or make a statement.
- Common helping verbs are *am, are, is, was, were, have, has, had, do, does, did, be, being, been, will, shall, can, could, would, should, might, must.*
- Main and helping verbs form different verb tenses.

Mechanics

- A contraction is a shortened form of two words.
- A contraction is made by combining a verb with the word *not*.

Read the sentences aloud. Write the corrected sentences, making sure that the verb phrases and contractions are correct.

1. Anthony's band mates wasn't happy with his trombone playing.

   _____

   _____

2. Anthony's cousin will be come to pick up Anthony this morning.

   _____

   _____

3. Anthony's band leader tells him that if he attend practice, his playing will improved.

   _____

   _____

4. Anthony is always wanted to be in two places at once.

   _____

   _____

5. Anthony's friends have recognized the song he play.

   _____

At Home: Write two sentences in which you use two of the helping verbs above.

Name_____

> • **A linking verb** does not show action. It links the subject to a noun or an adjective in the predicate.
> • Common linking verbs are *am, is, are, was, were, be, being, been, seem, feel, appear, become, look, taste, smell.*

In the space provided, write the linking verbs in each of the following sentences.

1. It is an ordinary day. _____

2. The three farmers feel happy. _____

3. The crop looks like a good one. _____

4. Suddenly someone appears at the edge of the field. _____

5. It looks like one of the farmer's children. _____

6. She seems upset. _____

7. She is crying. _____

8. Now her father is worried. _____

9. The scientists felt good about their discovery. _____

10. The scientists could be next year's prize winners. _____

11. It seems that something is very wrong. _____

12. But it appears that the girl is mistaken. _____

At Home: Determine whether the subjects in the ten sentences above are singular or plural.

© Macmillan/McGraw-Hill

Name_____

- A **predicate noun** follows a linking verb and renames or identifies the subject.
- A **predicate adjective** follows a linking verb and describes the subject.

In the space provided, write the predicate noun or predicate adjective in the following sentences. Also, identify the word as either a predicate noun or a predicate adjective.

1. The archaeologists felt happy.

   _____

2. Terracotta soldiers were the work of people in northern China.

   _____

3. The soldiers are a source of information for historians.

   _____

4. The soldiers seem real.

   _____

5. The men who created them are gone.

   _____

6. Their names are unknown.

   _____

7. The archaeologists could become prize winners.

   _____

8. The soldiers are a reminder of past glory.

   _____

9. Every soldier looks different.

   _____

10. They are truly works of art.

   _____

At Home: Choose five of the predicate nouns or adjectives above and write sentences using them.

© Macmillan/McGraw-Hill

Name_____

- Capitalize the first, last, and all important words in a title.
- Underline or use italics for titles of books, plays, newspapers, magazines, movies, and TV series.

Capitalize and underline the following titles as they should appear. Write the correct titles on the lines provided.

1. the king and i

_____

2. martin's dictionary for kids

_____

3. tales by phantoms

_____

4. the digitopolis gazette

_____

Complete the following sentences with appropriate titles.

5. My favorite funny book is called _____.

6. It is even funnier than _____.

7. Have you ordered tickets to _____?

8. Because my uncle likes science, he subscribes to the magazine

_____

9. I watch the TV series _____ on Saturday evenings.

10. I was really sorry when _____ went off the air.

11. Linda will bring _____ for our newspaper study on Friday.

12. How eager I am to see the movie _____.

At Home: Find titles of books, plays, newspapers, magazines, movies, and TV series.

The Emperor's Silent Army   85
Grade 6/Unit 3

© Macmillan/McGraw-Hill

Name_____

> - A **linking verb** does not show action. It links the subject to a noun or an adjective in the predicate.
> - Common linking verbs are *am, is, are, was, were, be, being, been, seem, feel, appear, become, look, taste, smell.*

The writer of this short story did not proofread for mistakes. Rewrite the story correcting any mistakes made with linking verbs.

Lee, a young archaeologist, was work on an important site in northern China. It was his first dig, and he was nervous. The dean of the school of archaeology was watched him carefully. The dean was expect Lee to make a big mistake. Lee, however, was very careful. One morning, when Lee had already be digging for hours, his tiny shovel hit something solid. Lee know immediately that it is not stone. He gingerly lifted the piece from the sand. It are an arm band, an exquisite piece of gold jewelry. Lee stand up carefully, hold his prize, and heading for the dean's tent.

_____
_____
_____
_____
_____
_____
_____
_____
_____
_____
_____
_____

At Home: Write a short story about an important archaeological find. Use at least two linking verbs in your writing.

© Macmillan/McGraw-Hill

Name_____

Circle the letter of the choice that corrects each numbered sentence. If there is no error in the sentence, circle _c_ for _correct_.

1. The workers was excited.

   a. The workers were excited.

   b. The workers are looking excite.

   c. correct

2. The clanging of the shovels sounds distant.

   a. The clanging of the shovels sound distant.

   b. The clanging of the shovels have sounded distant.

   c. correct

3. People have grown more aware of archaeology.

   a. People has grown more aware of archaeology.

   b. People are grown more aware of archaeology.

   c. correct

4. The terracotta soldiers looks real.

   a. The terracotta soldiers looking real.

   b. The terracotta soldiers look real.

   c. correct

5. The archaeologists growed impatient as they continued to dig.

   a. The archaeologists grew impatient as they continued to dig.

   b. The archaeologists growing impatient as they continued to dig.

   c. correct

6. The names of the archaeologists is unknown.

   a. The names of the archaeologists be unknown.

   b. The names of the archaeologists are unknown.

   c. correct

The writer of this letter did not proofread for mistakes. Rewrite the letter correcting any mistakes made with linking verbs, colons, and commas.

May 15 2006

Dear Ms. Cummings

I am interesting in know about any classes in archaeology been held this summer for middle school students. I is currently in the sixth grade at Kennedy Middle School here in Topeka. I have reading a lot of books about archaeology, but I am wanting a more direct experience. Please send any information to the address above.

Sincerely

Jahlani Washington

_____
_____
_____
_____
_____
_____
_____
_____
_____
_____
_____
_____

At Home: Write a business letter requesting information from a museum on the topic of your choosing.

© Macmillan/McGraw-Hill

Name_____

- An **irregular verb** is a verb that does not add -*ed* to form the past tense.

Present	Past
think	thought
tear	tore
sink	sank
catch	caught
freeze	froze
break	broke
blow	blew
teach	taught
wear	wore
know	knew
drink	drank
choose	chose
speak	spoke

Correct errors in verb tenses in the following sentences.

1. The sound of applause breaked the silence of the theater.

   _____

2. Sarah knowed how wonderful it would be! _____

3. Sarah catched the bouquet that was thrown onto the stage.

   _____

4. Sarah's father blowed her a kiss from the audience. _____

5. She almost teared her costume as she made a deep bow.

   _____

6. Sarah often thinked about poetry. _____

At Home: Pick out irregular verbs from a newspaper or magazine article and add them to the list.

The Case of the Phantom Poet **89**
Grade 6/Unit 3

- Some irregular verbs have special spellings when used with the helping verbs *have, has,* or *had.*

Present	Past	Past (with *have, has, had*)
think	thought	thought
tear	tore	torn
sink	sank	sunk
catch	caught	caught
freeze	froze	frozen
break	broke	broken
blow	blew	blown
teach	taught	taught
wear	wore	worn
know	knew	known
drink	drank	drunk
choose	chose	chosen
speak	spoke	spoken

Each sentence contains an incorrect form of an irregular verb. Write the correct verb form on the line provided.

1. As soon as Sarah stepped out onto the stage, she freezed.

_____

2. Albert finally finded the prop he needed for Act Two. _____

3. Sarah had speaked with the director about her lines in Act One.

_____

4. She thinked that the speech was too long. _____

5. But the director had choosed Sarah for a reason; he knew she could do it.

_____

At Home: Choose five verbs from the chart and write sentences for each, using the correct form.

© Macmillan/McGraw-Hill

Name_____

- A play consists of characters, setting, stage directions, and dialogue.
- Setting is shown in italic print.
- Characters' names are indented and followed by a colon.
- Stage directions are shown in parentheses and in italic print, following the colon after the character's name.
- Dialogue is shown without quotation marks following a character's name.

Add or delete punctuation in the following play. Underline words that should be in italic print. Correct any mistakes in verb form.

Scene 1

The kitchen; Sarah and her sister are sit at the kitchen table.

_____

_____

Sarah (upset, close to tears) "I can't do it, Barb! I can't star in the school play!"

_____

_____

Barb: Of course you can. Remember when you starring in *Cinderella* in the fourth grade? You even sanged a solo!"

_____

_____

Sarah (recovering; wiping her eyes) "Yes, yes, you're right."

_____

_____

Barb : And everybody clapping! Remember?"

_____

At Home: Write a short play dialogue, using correct punctuation and the correct verb forms.

The writer of this play dialogue did not proofread for mistakes. Rewrite the dialogue correcting any mistakes made in punctuating the scene. Make sure verb forms are used correctly.

Scene 1

LaWonda on stage at rehearsal. With her is Danny and Sarah.

LaWonda loudly "Danny, you keep standed in front of Sarah! You're supposing to be behind her.

Danny defiantly "Who making you boss?"

LaWonda gesturing with the script "See? It sayed so right here!"

Sarah looked at her script, then pointing backstage "She's right, Danny. You belonged back there."

Danny sighing, then walking backstage "Two against one. Okay."

_____

_____

_____

_____

_____

_____

_____

_____

_____

_____

_____

At Home: Write a dialogue where actors disagree with each other.

Name_____

A. Write the past tense of each verb below.

1. wear   _____

2. think   _____

3. blow   _____

4. drink   _____

5. speak   _____

B. Use the past participle of each verb in a sentence of your own.

6. freeze _____

7. catch _____

8. tear _____

9. choose _____

10. know _____

11. teach _____

12. break _____

Name_____

- An **irregular verb** is a verb that does not add *-ed* to the past tense.
- Some irregular verbs have special spellings when used with the helping verbs *have, has,* or *had.*

Mechanics

- Use a comma to show a pause after an introductory word, such as *well*.
- Use commas to set off words that interrupt the flow of thought in a sentence, such as *of course*.
- Use commas to set off nouns of direct address.

Rewrite the sentences. Use the correct form of the irregular verb and insert commas where they are needed.

1. Mrs. Torrington has Sarah already speaked to you?

_____

2. Of course Sarah already knowed her lines!

_____

3. Well I hadn't thinked about that yet!

_____

4. Have you choosed what you are going to wear on opening night?

_____

_____

Read the passage and look at each underlined word. How would you describe the word? Circle the letter of your answer.

Sarah sees a lot of old <u>movies</u>. The <u>comedies</u> of Frank Capra are among her
              (1)   (2)

favorites. She especially likes <u>A Pocketful of Miracles</u> and <u>A Hole in the</u>

<u>Head</u>.

1. **A.** active verb
   B. direct object
   C. indirect object
   D. subject

2. **A.** direct object
   B. indirect object
   C. subject
   D. predicate

Read the passage and look at the underlined sentences. Is there a mistake? If there is, how would you correct it? Circle the letter of your answer.

<u>Sarah has finally teached herself how to be confident onstage. It has tooken</u>
              (3)

<u>lots of time and practice. Sarah finally knows that the butterflies she feels in her</u>
   (4)   (5)

<u>stomach are simply excitement, not fright.</u>

3. **A.** Change *teached* to *teach*.
   B. Change *teached* to *had teached*.
   C. Change *teached* to *taught*.
   D. No mistake

4. **A.** Change *has tooken* to *has took*.
   B. Change *has tooken* to *taked*.
   C. Change *has tooken* to *has taken*.
   D. No mistake

5. **A.** Change *knows* to *known*.
   B. Change *knows* to *knowing*.
   C. Change *knows* to *knowed*.
   D. No mistake

© Macmillan/McGraw-Hill

Sarah always drinked a big glass of orange juice and a big glass of water
<u>   </u>
(6)

before a performance. She has saying the drinks keep her throat from getting
<u>   </u>
(7)

dry. I think that she may be right.
<u>   </u>
(8)

6. **A.** Change *drinked* to *drinking*.
    B. Change *drinked* to *drink*.
    C. Change *drinked* to *drank*.
    D. No mistake

7. **A.** Change *has saying* to *has says*.
    B. Change *has saying* to *has saids*.
    C. Change *has saying* to *has said*.
    D. No mistake

8. **A.** Change *think* to *thinking*.
    B. Change *think* to *thinked*.
    C. Change *think* to *thunk*.
    D. No mistake

Danny, however, has always wear his polka-dot socks onstage. He chooses to
<u>   </u>
(9)

believe that the socks give him good luck. Whatever it takes, Danny!
<u>   </u>
(10)

9. **A.** Change *has always wear* to *has always worn*.
    B. Change *has always wear* to *has always weared*.
    C. Change *has always wear* to *has always wearing*.
    D. No mistake

10. **A.** Change *chooses* to *choosed*.
    B. Change *chooses* to *choosing*.
    C. Change *chooses* to *choose*.
    D. No mistake

© Macmillan/McGraw-Hill

Name_____

- A **pronoun** is a word that takes the place of one or more nouns.
- The **antecedent** or **referent** of a pronoun is the word or group of words to which the pronoun refers. Pronouns and antecedents must agree.

Write a pronoun to take the place of the underlined noun or noun phrase. Write your answer on the line provided.

1. <u>Erik</u> has climbed many mountains. _____

2. <u>Climbers</u> take special equipment with them. _____

3. <u>Erik</u> believes in proper training before a climb. _____

4. <u>Erik's partners</u> try to stay in contact during a climb. _____

5. Has <u>Peter</u> seen the movie about Mount Everest? _____

Write the pronoun in the parentheses that agrees with its underlined antecedent on the line provided.

6. <u>Erik</u> knew that (he, she) wanted to live a full life. _____

7. <u>Erik's friends</u> asked if (she, they) could attend his marriage on a mountain. _____

8. Climbers need <u>ice axes</u>, and I have seen one of (he, them).

   _____

9. When <u>Peter</u> talked to us about climbing, (he, she) was serious.

   _____

10. Peter tried to repair <u>the radio</u>, but (they, it) still would not work.

   _____

At Home: Have the student use ten pronouns to write a short story about climbing a mountain.

Seeing Things His Own Way
Grade 6/Unit 4
97

© Macmillan/McGraw-Hill

Name_____

- Singular pronouns are *I, you, he, she, it, me, him,* and *her*.
- Plural pronouns are *we, you, they, us,* and *them*.

Fill in the blank with an appropriate pronoun. Write an *S* if the pronoun is singular. Write a *P* if the pronoun is plural.

1. _____ wonder if Peter will come hiking. _____

2. After breakfast, _____ went on a hike. _____

3. The hikers take plenty of water with _____.
_____

4. Will Peter and Susanna hike with _____? _____

5. Spanish is an interesting language, and _____ is easy to
learn. _____

6. _____ is interested in studying Spanish. _____

7. Peter signed up for a language class, and then _____ bought
the books for it. _____

8. The language school was far away, but Peter enjoyed walking to
_____. _____

9. Peter and Susanna both studied Spanish, and then _____
studied French. _____

10. Peter called Susanna and asked _____ to lunch.
_____

At Home: Have the student write a sentence for each pronoun used in the sentences above.

- A **pronoun** is a word that takes the place of one or more nouns.
- The **antecedent** or **referent** of a pronoun is the word or group of words to which the pronoun refers. Pronouns and antecedents must agree.
- Singular pronouns are *I, you, he, she, it, me, him, her.*
- Plural pronouns are *we, you, they, us, them.*

Choose the pronoun in parentheses that correctly completes each sentence. Write it on the line provided.

1. During the hike, (he, they) talk to each other. _____
2. (We, She) take peanut butter crackers for a snack. _____
3. (It, They) know that it is dangerous to hike after dark. _____
4. Take (me, they) with you. _____
5. Peter called Susanna, and (she, it) answered the phone.

   _____

Write an appropriate pronoun on the line.

6. _____ hopes to come on the hike with us.
7. Will _____ be my hiking buddy?
8. _____ both promised to come that weekend.
9. Peter was so happy that _____ could come.
10. Susanna said that _____ will be leaving at dawn.
11. _____ sound like interesting characters.
12. Will _____ watch my favorite television program with me tonight?

At Home: Have the student choose 5 pronouns from the sentences above and write sentences about a fictional outing.

Seeing Things His Own Way **99**
Grade 6/Unit 4

© Macmillan/McGraw-Hill

Name_____

- A **pronoun** is a word that takes the place of one or more nouns.
- The **antecedent** or **referent** of a pronoun is the word or group of words to which the pronoun refers. Pronouns and antecedents must agree.

Underline any pronouns that do not agree with their antecedents. Then rewrite the interview, using the correct singular and plural pronouns, capitalization, and punctuation.

I interviewed Brian Plomaco the famed one-armed mountaineer from utah. I asked you how it feels to be so accomplished Brian noted that Everyone wants their chance to do something great so you feel really lucky.

Brian and his Crew have climbed many Mountains, and he worked hard. Brian says that every Climber first need the right gear which will make your climb safer.

_____
_____
_____
_____
_____
_____
_____
_____
_____
_____

At Home: Have the student write an imaginary interview with an uncommon champion of his or her choice.

Name_____

Choose the pronoun in parentheses that correctly completes the following sentences. Write it on the line provided.

1. Peter brought the climbing ropes, and then he checked (them, it).

   _____

2. Susanna read the hiking manual and returned (it, him) to the library.

   _____

3. Peter tells Susanna (he, we) is glad she's going on the hike.

   _____

4. Peter, will (you, her) e-mail your reply today? _____

5. Susanna likes orange juice, and so (she, it) brought some along.

   _____

Put brackets [ ] around each pronoun in the following sentences. Write the pronoun's antecedent on the line provided.

6. Susanna is going on the hike, and Peter is going with _____.

   _____

7. Peter wrote a letter and then mailed _____.

   _____

8. Peter likes apples and eats a lot of _____.

   _____

9. Peter's instructions help _____, the beginners, have a safe

   day. _____

10. Peter and Susanna saw the movie, but they did not like

    _____. _____

> - A **pronoun** is a word that takes the place of one or more nouns.
> - The **antecedent** or **referent** of a pronoun is the word or group of words to which the pronoun refers. Pronouns and antecedents must agree.
> - Singular pronouns are *I, you, he, she, it, me, him, her*.
> - Plural pronouns are *we, you, they, us, them*.

Look at the picture. Add a singular or plural pronoun to complete each sentence based on the picture.

1. Peter invited Susanna on a hike, and _____ left this morning.

2. Susanna wants some water, and Peter will give _____ to her.

3. Peter said, "Is it okay if _____ hike until lunchtime?"

4. Susanna's backpack is too heavy, and _____ is hurting her shoulders.

5. Peter said, "Why don't _____ take a short rest."

© Macmillan/McGraw-Hill

Name_____

> • A **subject pronoun** is used as the subject of a sentence.
> • Use a subject pronoun when the pronoun is part of a compound subject.
> • *I, you, he, she, it, we,* and *they* are subject pronouns.

Choose the correct pronoun in parentheses to complete each sentence. Write it on the line provided.

1. Janis and (I, me) _____ are going to learn how to scuba dive.

2. (She, Her) _____ has already tried on her diving mask.

3. All of the other divers and (she, her) _____ jumped into the water.

4. (They, Them) _____ were totally fearless.

5. But (I, me) _____ was hesitating.

Read each sentence and put brackets [ ] around any incorrect subject pronoun. Rewrite each sentence correctly on the line provided. If the pronoun is correct, write *Correct* instead of the sentence.

6. said to me, "Rosie, just get your feet wet!"

   _____

7. all laughed at me.

   _____

8. Janis said, "You and will go into the water together."

   _____

9. and our teacher took me by the hands.

   _____

10. We all jumped into the water together.

   _____

© Macmillan/McGraw-Hill

At Home: Have the student write three sentences using
subject pronouns.

Name_____

- An **object pronoun** is used as the object of a verb or as the object of a preposition, such as *for, at, with,* or *to.*
- Use an object pronoun when the pronoun is part of a compound object.
- *Me, you, him, her, it, us,* and *them* are object pronouns.

Put brackets [ ] around each incorrect object pronoun. Write the correct object pronoun on the line.

1. Janis tried not to laugh at I. _____

2. The diving teacher handed the flippers to she. _____

3. Raul said, "Please bring these flippers to they."_____

4. Will Janis come into the water with Raul and I? _____

5. Between you and I, scuba diving is a little scary. _____

6. I finally learned how to dive, and it brought I great happiness.

_____

Put brackets around the object pronoun in parentheses that correctly completes each sentence.

7. The teacher cried out, "Jump!" to Janis and (I, me).

8. I looked at the deep water and tried not to think about (it, I).

9. Janis asked (they, them) to wait a moment longer for me.

10. She asked, "Won't you come diving with (we, us)?"

At Home: Have the student write two more sentences, continuing the story.

© Macmillan/McGraw-Hill

Name_____

- A **subject pronoun** is used as the subject of a sentence. Use a subject pronoun when the pronoun is part of a compound subject. *I, you, he, she, it, we,* and *they* are subject pronouns.
- An **object pronoun** is used as the object of a verb or as the object of a preposition, such as *for, at, with,* or *to.* Use an object pronoun when the pronoun is part of a compound object. *Me, you, him, her, it, us,* and *them* are object pronouns.
- Always write the pronoun I with a capital letter. Use *I* or *me* last when talking about yourself and another person.

Proofread each sentence. Then rewrite the sentence using the correct subject or object pronoun.

1. Do you think them will enjoy a day at the beach?

_____

2. I and Kasey want to go surfing.

_____

3. Kasey waxed the boards for he and Sam.

_____

4. Them shouted, "Don't forget to put on sunscreen!"

_____

5. "Why can't you take I, too?" asked Janis.

_____

6. The wind was so strong, they created waves that were ten feet high.

_____

_____

At Home: Have the student write a dialogue between two surfers getting ready to surf.

Name_____

- A **subject pronoun** is used as the subject of a sentence. Use a subject pronoun when the pronoun is part of a compound subject. *I, you, he, she, it, we,* and *they* are subject pronouns.
- An **object pronoun** is used as the object of a verb or as the object of a preposition, such as *for, at, with,* or *to*. Use an object pronoun when the pronoun is part of a compound object. *Me, you, him, her, it, us,* and *them* are object pronouns.

Proofread and rewrite the scientific observation using the correct subject and object pronoun. Correct capitalization and punctuation.

This was my first time SCUBA diving. i took several weeks of classes at the YMCA to get certified. I and my instructor spent hours in the pool, and i was excited as i strapped on my gear and tipped into the water. The first animal me saw was a moray eel! Me had been warned about eels, which like to stay in shallow water and hide under rocks. Him was beautifully colored and at least three feet long. me and my instructor truly enjoyed seeing this incredible animal up close.

_____

_____

_____

_____

_____

_____

_____

_____

At Home: Have the student write an imaginary observation of something he or she would like to see up close while scuba diving.

Read the first sentence of each set. One of the four sentences that follow correctly replaces the underlined subject with a subject pronoun. Circle the letter of the correct sentence.

1. Janis and Raul learned to scuba dive last summer.
   a. Them learned to scuba dive last summer.
   b. They learned to scuba dive last summer.
   c. Raul learned to scuba dive last summer.
   d. I learned to scuba dive last summer.

2. Raul was the first to be certified.
   a. Her was the first to be certified.
   b. They was the first to be certified.
   c. He was the first to be certified.
   d. Him was the first to be certified.

3. My family and I will take a trip to the Gulf of Mexico next summer.
   a. Them will take a trip to the Gulf of Mexico next summer.
   b. They will take a trip to the Gulf of Mexico next summer.
   c. Me and my family will take a trip to the Gulf of Mexico next summer.
   d. We will take a trip to the Gulf of Mexico next summer.

Read the first sentence of each set. One of the four sentences that follows correctly replaces the underlined object with an object pronoun. Circle the letter of the correct sentence.

4. Raul warned Janis and me not to swim out too far.
   a. Raul warned Janis and I not to swim out too far.
   b. Raul warned us not to swim out too far.
   c. Raul warned they not to swim out too far.
   d. Raul warned them not to swim out too far.

5. He showed Paul and Sam how to use their flippers.
   a. He showed them how to use their flippers.
   b. He showed they how to use their flippers.
   c. He showed we how to use their flippers.
   d. He showed him how to use their flippers.

6. Janis said she and Raul had decided to come back every year.
   a. I   c. them
   b. us   d. they

Name_____

- A **subject pronoun** is used as the subject of a sentence. Use a subject pronoun when the pronoun is part of a compound subject. *I, you, he, she, it, we,* and *they* are subject pronouns.
- An **object pronoun** is used as the object of a verb or as the object of a preposition, such as *for, at, with,* or *to*. Use an object pronoun when the pronoun is part of a compound object. *Me, you, him, her, it, us,* and *them* are object pronouns.

Mechanics

- Always write the pronoun I with a capital letter.
- Use I or me last when talking about yourself and another person.

Read each sentence aloud. Choose the subject or object pronoun in parentheses that correctly completes each sentence. Rewrite the sentence correctly on the line provided.

1. (Her, She) and my sister wished they could go snorkeling.

_____

2. Seeing some colorful fish would be a treat for (they, them).

_____

3. "Why can't you take your sister with (you, they)?" asked Mother.

_____

4. "But (us, we) don't have room in the car," I answered.

_____

5. "I'm sure you can squeeze (she, her) in," replied Mother.

_____

6. "As long as (us, we) can all get along!" I exclaimed.

_____

Name_____

- A **possessive pronoun** takes the place of a possessive noun. It shows *who* or *what* owns something.
- Some possessive pronouns are used before nouns (*my, you, his, her, its, our, your, their*.)

Read each sentence. Write the possessive pronoun on the line.

1. Let me tell you about my summer of 2004. _____

2. That was the summer that four hurricanes swept through our state of Florida. _____

3. Many people lost their electricity for weeks. _____

4. Mr. Sanchez saw the roof of his house blow off. _____

5. Mrs. Sanchez watched as a pine tree fell on her car. _____

6. Our eyes were glued to the weather channel. _____

7. We watched each huge, swirling storm make its way closer to town. _____

8. Father said, "Do you have batteries for your radio?" _____

9. He asked our neighbors also. _____

10. They did not have any for their radio, so we gave them some. _____

11. You can borrow my radio, but please return it. _____

12. Do you have a special place to set up your radio? _____

© Macmillan/McGraw-Hill

At Home: Have the student make a list of five possessive nouns.

Name_____

- Some possessive pronouns can stand alone (*mine, yours, his, hers, its, ours, yours, theirs.*)
- Do not confuse the pronouns *its, your, their,* and *theirs* with the contractions *it's, you're, they're,* and *there's.*

Find the possessive pronoun in each of the following sentences. Write it on the line.

1. The patio chairs that blew into the neighbors' yard are not ours.

   _____

2. Mr. Sanchez looked at them, but they were not his. _____

3. The red bicycle, however, is mine. _____

4. The Laninghams finally identified the patio chairs as theirs.

   _____

5. Mrs. York said that the flower pot was hers. _____

Circle the pronoun in parentheses that correctly completes each sentence.

6. Is the bicycle (you'res, yours)?

7. (It's, Its) handlebars are totally rusted from the rain.

8. The car that the tree fell on is (theirs, there's).

9. (My, Mine) is the gray car in the driveway.

10. Two of (it's, its) tires are flat.

11. Is the battery pack (you'res, yours)?

12. I believe it is (theirs, there's).

At Home: Have the student choose four of the possessive pronouns above and write sentences with them.

© Macmillan/McGraw-Hill

Name_____

- Use quotation marks before and after the words of a direct quotation.
- Use a comma before a quotation when the speaker's name comes first.
- Use a comma, a question mark, or an exclamation point to end the quotation when the speaker's name comes last.

Rewrite each sentence using the correct punctuation.

1. Listen to the wind cried Pablo

_____

2. Marissa asked Do you think we will lose our power

_____

3. I hope not said Mother

_____

4. We have peanut butter, don't we asked Pablo

_____

5. Mother said We have cans of tuna fish, too

_____

6. But we have only an electric can opener cried Pablo

7. He said If we lose our electricity, we won't be able to open any cans

_____

_____

8. Don't worry said Mother

_____

9. There is a can opener in the bottom drawer she said

_____

10. I'll make sure it works said Pablo

At Home: Have the student write a dialogue he or she might have with a friend during a rain- or snowstorm.

Name_____

> - A **possessive pronoun** takes the place of a possessive noun. It shows who or what owns something.
> - Some possessive pronouns are used before nouns (*my, you, his, her, its, our, your, their*).

Correct any errors in the use of possessive pronouns, contractions, punctuation, or capitalization in the fictional narrative below. Then rewrite the narrative.

"How can I help?"

This was the only thought on young Pablo's mind after the hurricane as he looked at the fallen trees toppled power lines and homes without roofs in there town. "Is that bicycle you'res asked Mr. Sanchez.

Pablo said "Yes, its mine."

"Then jump on it's seat and ride to the community center. you can help make ten thousand ham and cheese sandwiches for folks who were evacuated.

_____

_____

_____

_____

_____

_____

_____

_____

_____

_____

© Macmillan/McGraw-Hill

At Home: Have the student write a fictional narrative about a young boy or girl who helps after a storm.

Choose the correct possessive pronoun or contraction in parentheses. Then write the sentence correctly on the line.

1. "Wash (you're, your) hands before you start making sandwiches," said Mrs. Chu.

   _____

   _____

2. Pablo and (he, his) partner put mustard on the bread.

   _____

3. "Do you have (my, mine) extra knife?" asked Mrs. Chu.

   _____

4. "I thought it was (you'res, yours)," said Pablo.

   _____

5. "(Its, It's) now time to start putting on the cheese," said Mrs. Chu.

   _____

   _____

6. "Where should we put (our, ours) sandwiches when we're done?" asked Pablo.

   _____

   _____

7. The children reacted to (their, they're) news with enthusiasm.

   _____

   _____

8. I don't want to eat the sandwich if (it's, its) yours.

   _____

   _____

Name_____

- A **possessive pronoun** takes the place of a possessive noun. It shows who or what owns something.
- Some possessive pronouns are used before nouns (*my, you, his, her, its, our, your, their*).

Mechanics

- Some possessive pronouns can stand alone (*mine, yours, his, hers, its, ours, yours, theirs*).
- Do not confuse the pronouns *its, your, their,* and *theirs* with the contractions *it's, you're, they're,* and *there's*.
- An apostrophe take the place of letters left out of a contraction. Possessive pronouns do not have apostrophes.

Read the sentences. Choose the possessive pronoun in parentheses that correctly completes each sentence. Then rewrite the sentence on the line provided.

1. (My, Mine) cousin Pablo helped out after the hurricane.

_____

2. The town he worked in was (ours, you'res).

_____

3. They were amazed at the storm and (its, it's) power.

_____

4. When the helpers finish, the satisfaction will be (there's, theirs).

_____

© Macmillan/McGraw-Hill

At Home: Ask the student to write two sentences in which he or she use two of the possessive pronouns above.

Name_____

- An **indefinite pronoun** does not refer to a particular person, place, or thing.
- Use a singular verb with a singular indefinite pronoun, such as *anybody, anyone, anything, each, everybody, everyone, everything, nobody, nothing, somebody, someone,* or *something.*

Read each sentence. Choose the verb in parentheses that correctly completes the sentence and write it on the line provided.

1. Everybody (is, are) hoping to attend the bicycle race today.

   _____

2. Each of the riders (is, are) ready. _____

3. Everything (need, needs) to be cleaned up on the racing track.

   _____

4. Somebody (deliver, delivers) water to the racers as they ride.

   _____

5. If anyone (ask, asks), I am rooting for my sister, Samantha.

   _____

Change the singular or plural verb in each sentence so that it agrees with the indefinite pronoun. Then rewrite the sentence.

6. Somebody must helps me set up the beverage cart.

   _____

7. Everyone agree that it is a perfect day for cycling.

   _____

8. No one are more excited than I about the race.

   _____

9. Nothing seem impossible today.

   _____

10. Everybody wait for the race to begin.

    _____

© Macmillan/McGraw-Hill

At Home: Have the student find and underline indefinite pronouns in a newspaper or magazine article.

Name_____

> • Use a plural verb with a plural indefinite pronoun, such as *both,*
> *few, many, others,* or *several.*

**Read each sentence. Choose the verb in parentheses that correctly
completes the sentence and write it on the line provided.**

1. Many of us (enjoys, enjoy) cycling. _____

2. A few (rides, ride) every morning. _____

3. Both of them (wishes, wish) to win the cycling tournament.

   _____

4. Several of the riders (trains, train) with a coach. _____

5. Others (likes, like) to train on their own. _____

**Circle the indefinite pronoun. Write S if the indefinite pronoun is
singular. Write P if the indefinite pronoun is plural.**

6. A few of the riders wear special riding gloves. _____

7. Others have special riding helmets. _____

8. Somebody is here from the newspaper to cover the story.

   _____

9. The reporter said there was something exciting about every race.

   _____

10. Many cannot get seats and are standing on the grass. _____

At Home: Have the student choose five of the indefinite
pronouns above and write sentences using them.

© Macmillan/McGraw-Hill

Name_____

- Use a hyphen to show the division of a word at the end of a line. Divide the word between syllables.
- Use a hyphen in numbers from twenty-one through ninety-nine and in some other compound words.

Rewrite each word, using hyphens between syllables. Check your work in a dictionary, if necessary.

1. basement _____
2. toward _____
3. vacation _____
4. happening _____
5. pacific _____
6. fanciful _____
7. margarine _____
8. cabin _____

9. police _____
10. English _____
11. carbon _____
12. homemade _____
13. loyalty _____
14. innocence _____
15. Titanic _____

Use hyphens to write each number as words.

16. #99 _____
17. #58 _____
18. #35 _____
19. #89 _____
20. #76 _____
21. #39 _____
22. #22 _____
23. #51 _____
24. #68 _____

At Home: Have the student write six lines of a newspaper story about a bicycle race. Have him or her hyphenate a word at the end of each line.

Name _____

- An **indefinite pronoun** does not refer to a particular person, place, or thing.
- Use a singular verb with a singular indefinite pronoun, such as *anybody, anyone, anything, each, everybody, everyone, everything, nobody, nothing, somebody, someone,* or *something*.
- Use a plural verb with a plural indefinite pronoun, such as *both, few, many, others,* or *several*.

Proofread this news article. Then rewrite the article using the correct singular or plural verb. Correct any mistakes in punctuation.

Samantha Higgins, a twelve-year-old sixth grader from Memphis, Tennessee won the 30K Cycling Championship today in this city. Many fans believes that Samantha who completed the race in record time had an advantage with her clipless pedals. Clipless pedals locks into a cleat in the sole of a special cycling shoe. When asked what other tips she have for riders, Samantha said "Everybody must checks cadence. Few winning riders ignores maintenance. Everyone clean, lube and check the bike! Nobody ride without a helmet. Ever."

_____
_____
_____
_____
_____
_____
_____
_____
_____

© Macmillan/McGraw-Hill

At Home: Have the student write a fictional news article about how he or she won a race. Use at least three indefinite pronouns.

Read the first sentence of each set. One of the four sentences that follows corrects the agreement between an indefinite pronoun and its verb. Circle the letter of the correct sentence.

1. Each of the girls prefer this bike.
   a. Change *Each* to *Few.*
   b. Change *Each* to *Every.*
   c. Change *Each* to *One.*
   d. Change *prefer* to *preferring.*

2. Somebody like to ride each morning at dawn.
   a. Change *Somebody* to *Everyone.*
   b. Change *Somebody* to *Each.*
   c. Change *Somebody* to *Many.*
   d. Change *Somebody* to *Nobody.*

3. Everything about the race reminds cyclists that someone want to win.
   a. Change *reminds* to *remind.*
   b. Change *want* to *wants.*
   c. Change *someone* to *nobody.*
   d. Change *someone* to *no one.*

Circle the letter that best answers each of the following questions.

4. Which of the following statements about indefinite pronouns is true?
   a. Indefinite pronouns, such as several, use a singular verb.
   b. Indefinite pronouns take the place of certain people, places, or things.
   c. Indefinite pronouns, such as everyone, use a plural verb.
   d. Indefinite pronouns do not refer to a particular person, place, or thing.

5. Which of the following sentences contains an indefinite pronoun?
   a. My bicycle has a flat tire.
   b. Several have gone flat recently.
   c. The broken bike is his.
   d. She won the race by a slim margin.

6. Which of the following sentences uses an indefinite pronoun?
   a. Most kids have the older model of the bike.
   b. Few parents disagree that reflectors are necessary.
   c. Everyone likes to ride around the park.
   d. Several people think that blue is the best color for a bike.

Name_____

- An **indefinite pronoun** does not refer to a particular person, place, or thing.
- Use a singular verb with a singular indefinite pronoun, such as *anybody, anyone, anything, each, everybody, everyone, everything, nobody, nothing, somebody, someone,* or *something.*
- Use a plural verb with a plural indefinite pronoun, such as *both, few, many, others,* or *several.*

The writer of this news article did not proofread for mistakes. Read the article and then rewrite the article correcting any mistakes made with indefinite pronouns, punctuation, or capitalization.

DATELINE MEMPHIS—Samantha Higgins returned to her home city of memphis today wearing the gold medal for winning the Middle Grades 30K Cycling Championship in Atlanta last Saturday anybody who know Samantha know that she puts her all into everything she does many believes she will continue to win at cycling events around the country. each of her teammates feel that Samantha deserved to win because of her commitment to the sport. Congratulations, Sam! everyone wish you well?

_____

_____

_____

_____

_____

_____

_____

_____

© Macmillan/McGraw-Hill

Name_____

- Relative pronouns are used to link a clause to another noun or pronoun.
- Interrogative pronouns ask a question when an important noun in a sentence is not known.
- Who, whom, whose, and which can be either interrogative or relative pronouns. That is a relative pronoun, and what is an interrogative pronoun.

Turn the following statements into questions using the interrogative pronoun in parentheses. Write the question on the line provided.

1. She digs carefully each day at the site. (who)

_____

2. Making a piece of ceramic from the past is easy. (what)

_____

3. The archeologists are going to dig in China. (where)

_____

4. You are interested in this magazine or that magazine. (which)

_____

5. These tools can be used to build the wall. (what)

_____

Choose the correct relative pronoun to complete each sentence. Write the corrected sentence on the line provided.

6. Bill is the scientist (who, whom) you met last June.

_____

7. The builders are people (whose, which) work we depend on.

_____

8. This is the book (what, that) I told you about.

_____

At Home: Have the student draw an arrow from the subject pronoun to the verb with which it agrees.

- Verbs must also agree with indefinite pronouns.

Rewrite each sentence, choosing the verb in parentheses that agrees with the indefinite pronoun.

1. Everything (is, are) incredibly interesting at an archaeological dig.

   _____

   _____

2. No one (deny, denies) that the work is extremely difficult.

   _____

3. Both of the archaeologists (work, works) at a major university.

   _____

4. A few of the volunteers (is, are) students at the school.

   _____

5. Nobody (make, makes) much money as a volunteer on a dig.

   _____

6. Everyone (know, knows) that the pleasure is in the possibility of discovery.

   _____

   _____

7. Others (claim, claims) that they most enjoy the countries they get to visit.

   _____

   _____

8. (Do, Does) anybody want to volunteer for a dig in Arizona?

   _____

9. Many (have, has) already signed up.

   _____

10. Several (want, wants) to sign up for the dig in Oregon.

    _____

At Home: Have the student underline each indefinite pronoun above and label whether each is singular or plural.

Name_____

- Pay careful attention to the spelling of homophones (words that sound alike) in your writing.
- Some common homophones and their correct usage are shown in the chart below.

Word

there	two	your	our
their	too	you're	hour
they're	who's	it's	here
to	whose	its	hear

Correct Usage

There is a lecture at noon today.

Their class is also at noon.

They're going to attend class at noon.

Are you going to class today?

Two students were absent.

Alicia was absent, too.

Who's coming to lunch with me?

Whose bike is outside the classroom?

Your bike is next to mine.

You're going to be late for class.

It's going to be a sunny day.

The school is proud of its teachers.

Our teacher is Mrs. Brookline.

Class begins one hour from now.

Here is your textbook for class.

I would like to hear this lecture.

Read the sentence below. Choose the word in parentheses that correctly completes each sentence. Rewrite the sentence on the line provided.

1. (There, Their, They're) is going to be a program on TV about a dig in England.

_____

_____

2. (Whose, Who's) going to narrate the program?

_____

© Macmillan/McGraw-Hill

At Home: Ask the student to choose three homophones from the list above and write sentences for each.

A Single Shard • Grade 6/Unit 4 (123)

Name_____

- A verb must agree with its subject pronoun.

Pronouns	Verbs
He, she it	walks, is, was, has
We, you, they	walk, are, were, have
I	walk, am, was, have

- Verbs must also agree with indefinite pronouns.
- Use a singular verb with a singular indefinite pronoun.
- Use a plural verb with a plural indefinite pronoun.

Proofread this magazine article. Then rewrite the article making sure verbs agree with subject nouns and pronouns. Correct any mistakes in punctuation.

During the third century, B.C.E., people who lived in the lands between the Tigris and Euphrates rivers founding the first cities. These people invents writing. They also creates architecture develops irrigation writes poetry and makes laws. They was an amazing civilization. Can anybody sees the art of the Sumerians and not marvel? Several works of art is on display this month at our local history museum. Everyone should visits.

_____

_____

_____

_____

_____

_____

_____

At Home: Invite the student to write a magazine article announcing a new exhibit, using several subject and indefinite pronouns.

© Macmillan/McGraw-Hill

Name _____

Write the verb in parentheses that correctly completes each sentence.

1. Everyone (has, have) to wear a hard hat at the archaeological site.
   _____

2. We (prefer, prefers) to work first thing in the morning. _____

3. She and Polly (has, have) studied the art of ancient Greece.

   _____

4. She (study, studies) in the evenings at the library. _____

5. Many (has, have) seen the exhibit at the history museum.

   _____

Write the pronoun in parentheses that correctly completes each sentence.

6. (Who, What) loves to study ancient Greece more than Polly?

   _____

7. Do (you, he) know the new professor of archaeology? _____

8. (Each, Few) know that she is the youngest professor in the school.

   _____

9. (We, He) hopes to study in Mexico this summer. _____

10. Among the choices (this, these) are the fastest computers to do research.

    _____

Name_____

- A verb must agree with its subject pronoun.

Pronouns	Verbs
He, she it	walks, is, was, has
We, you, they	walk, are, were, have
I	walk, am, was, have

Change the verb in the following sentences so that it agrees with the subject pronoun. Write your response on the line provided.

1. Everyone want to study in Mexico this summer. _____

2. I hopes that I will be able to travel there. _____

3. She take all her language classes in the afternoon. _____

4. Nothing bother her more than getting up too early. _____

Name_____

Pronouns

Read the passage. Circle the letter of the word that belongs in each space.

   Polly said, "Shameka and I ____(1)____ for the magazine, Dig It! It is very popular. I know that you ____(2)____ seen other kids reading it." Polly paused. Then she added, "Many pick up ____(3)____ copies at the school newsstand."

1. A. write
   B. writes
   C. written
   D. writing

2. A. has
   B. have
   C. hasn't
   D. had

3. A. they're
   B. their
   C. there
   D. them

   Shameka told ____(4)____ that she had finished writing her article for the magazine. She asked, "If you and Lori have time, will you proofread ____(5)____ for me?" She looked worried. "Of course," I said. "Do you want us to do it today after school?"

4. A. Lori and me
   B. me and Lori
   C. Lori and I
   D. I and Lori

5. F. her
   G. him
   H. it
   J. them

At Home: Ask the student to choose three indefinite pronouns and use them in sentences.

Name_____

Read the sentences below. What is the antecedent for each underlined pronoun? Circle the letter of your answer.

Lori needed to talk to Peter, so she called him on the phone. She and Polly
                                      (1)

wanted to know if he would drive them to the lecture at the high school the next
                                    (2)

evening. Peter agreed and said they could ride with him to the lecture.
                                                      (3)

1. **A.** Lori
   B. needed
   C. so
   D. phone

2. **A.** if
   B. Lori and Polly
   C. wanted
   D. lecture

3. **A.** agreed
   B. Peter
   C. with
   D. they

Read the sentences below. What form of pronoun is each underlined word?

I cannot find my textbook. I will ask Polly if I may use hers.
              (4)   (5)

4. **A.** Subject pronoun
   B. Indefinite pronoun
   C. Possessive pronoun
   D. Object pronoun

5. **A.** Indefinite pronoun
   B. Object pronoun
   C. Subject pronoun
   D. Possessive pronoun

© Macmillan/McGraw-Hill

At Home: Ask the student to write three sentences using pronouns of his or her choice.

Name_____

- An **adjective** is a word that modifies, or describes, a noun or pronoun and tells *what kind, how many,* or *which one.*
- A **predicate adjective** follows a linking verb and describes the subject.

Underline each adjective in the following sentences. (Some sentences have more than one adjective.)

1. Francisco had a difficult time writing English.
2. His teacher had a round face, a small nose, and blue eyes.
3. Francisco worked hard on his homework assignments.
4. He memorized long poems that he kept in his shirt pocket.
5. Francisco was a slow reader.
6. The apartment had four rooms with painted walls.
7. The dusty room was filled with ceramic statues.

Underline each predicate adjective in the following sentences. (Some sentences have more than one predicate adjective.)

8. The novel, *The Grapes of Wrath*, seemed long and difficult to Francisco.
9. Miss Bell looked upset.
10. Francisco was nervous.
11. Miss Bell's smile seemed friendly.
12. Like Francisco's family, the Joad family was poor.
13. To Mr. Bell, the rooms appeared old and uninhabited.
14. The first edition of the novel was expensive.

At Home: Together, write three sentences about a difficult school assignment using three adjectives or predicate adjectives.

Name_____

- A **demonstrative adjective** points out something and tells *which one* or *which ones.*
- Use *this* and *that* with singular nouns. Use *these* and *those* with plural nouns.
- *This* and *these* refer to nouns that are nearby; *that* and *those* refer to nouns that are farther away.

Study the demonstrative adjectives in parentheses. Write the demonstrative adjective that correctly completes each sentence on the line provided.

1. _____ essay is mine. (These, This)

2. The students must read _____ books for English class. (these, this)

3. _____ book is about a traveling family. (These, That)

4. Will you hand me _____ theater tickets? (those, that)

5. _____ essay got the highest grade in the class. (This, Those)

Complete each sentence with an appropriate demonstrative adjective.

6. Please get me _____ book on the highest shelf.

7. _____ oranges are the ones Juni likes best.

8. _____ novel is the one that we will be reading.

9. _____ oranges are the sweetest in the store.

10. _____ dress is what I want to wear tonight.

At Home: Have the student write a sentence for each demonstrative adjective used above.

Name_____

- A **proper adjective** is formed from a proper noun.
- A **proper noun** begins with a capital letter.
- A **proper adjective** begins with a capital letter.

Rewrite each sentence below on the line provided, using capitals for any proper nouns.

1. beatrix potter wrote *the tale of peter rabbit*.

_____

_____

2. henry wadsworth longfellow wrote the poem "the village blacksmith."

_____

_____

3. robert louis stevenson wrote the poem "my shadow."

_____

_____

On the line provided, write the proper adjective in each sentence. (Some sentences have more than one proper adjective.)

4. She enjoy novels by Italian authors. _____

5. It took a Herculean effort to finish that novel. _____

6. Italy is a country located on the Mediterranean coast. _____

7. Many students in Italy study the English language. _____

8. Many American museums contain works of art by Italian painters.

_____

9. A popular Renaissance painter from Italy is Michelangelo.

_____

10. His paintings and sculptures are found in many European museums.

_____

At Home: Have the student underline the words and phrases that helped him or her figure out each word's meaning.

Breaking Through • Grade 6/Unit 5   131

Name_____

- An **adjective** is a word that modifies, or describes, a noun or pronoun and tells *what kind, how many,* or *which one.*
- A **predicate adjective** follows a linking verb and describes the subject.
- A **demonstrative adjective** points out something and tells *which one* or *which ones.*
- A **proper adjective** is formed from a proper noun. Begin a proper adjective with a capital letter.

Proofread this speech. Then rewrite the speech, correcting any errors in the use of predicate, demonstrative, or proper adjectives. Correct any mistakes in the use of homophones, capitalization, or punctuation.

This mourning we honor Mr. Tyburn, whose retiring after forty years of teaching english at our middle school. I was fortunate to have this wonderful teacher last year in sixth grade. His guidance was crucial in encouraging me to read more and right more. He opened up the world of american literature to me. Because of Mr. Tyburn, I am planning on a career as a journalist. My mentor Mr. Tyburn arranged for me to work as an intern at our local newspaper. Thank you Mr. Tyburn for all your hard work and encouragement.

_____

_____

_____

_____

_____

_____

_____

_____

© Macmillan/McGraw-Hill

At Home: Invite the student to write a speech about a mentor in his or her life. Remind the student to make sure to use adjectives correctly.

Decide which word listed after each sentence is an adjective. Circle the letter of your answer.

1. Miss Bell's gentle smile reminded Francisco of his mother.
   a. reminded
   b. gentle
   c. smile
   d. mother

2. This is the book Miss Bell wants us to read.
   a. book
   b. wants
   c. read
   d. This

3. Books of English literature are in this box.
   a. English
   b. literature
   c. box
   d. in

4. I want to take these books out of the library.
   a. want
   b. these
   c. take
   d. library

5. The library books are on the shelf.
   a. shelf
   b. are
   c. library
   d. books

6. Nancy and her friend enjoy reading about foreign lands.
   a. about
   b. friend
   c. foreign
   d. his

Name_____

- An **adjective** is a word that modifies, or describes, a noun or pronoun and tells *what kind, how many,* or *which one.*
- A **predicate adjective** follows a linking verb and describes the subject.
- A **demonstrative adjective** points out something and tells *which one* or *which ones.*
- A **proper adjective** is formed from a proper noun. Begin a proper adjective with a capital letter.

Put brackets [ ] around the adjectives in the following sentences. Identify each adjective as *adjective, predicate adjective, demonstrative adjective, or proper adjective.*

1. Ramon was eager to read the book.

_____

2. These books belong to me.

_____

3. The book contains Spanish poetry.

_____

4. The librarian is wearing a blue sweater.

_____

5. The book was hidden behind the table.

_____

6. The book has a tattered cover.

_____

7. Ramon bought that book at the bazaar.

_____

8. I will not sell you any of the old books.

_____

Name_____

- The words *a, an,* and *the* are special adjectives called **articles**.
- Use *a* and *an* with singular nouns.
- Use *a* if the next word starts with a consonant sound.
- Use *an* if the next word starts with a vowel sound.

Study the pair of articles in each sentence. Underline the article that correctly completes the sentence.

1. Matthew and Andrew have (a, an) problem.
2. (A, The) time in the afternoon goes by too quickly.
3. What (a, an) annoying situation!
4. (The, A) homework never seemed to get done.
5. But (the, a) boys always had time to play games.
6. Baby robins open their mouths wide for (a, an) meal of worms.
7. In the summer months, (a, the) sun rises high in the sky.

Complete each sentence with the correct article: *a, an,* or *the*. (More than one answer may be correct.)

8. Matthew and Andrew tried to figure out _____ solution to the problem.
9. They finally came up with _____ idea.
10. Matthew said, "Maybe we could do _____ homework before we play games."
11. Andrew wasn't sure he liked _____ solution.
12. Matthew said, "I think this is _____ case of some smart thinking!"
13. Sometimes you can see _____ rainbow in the sky after it rains.
14. Matthew goes to _____ chess class on Tuesday.

© Macmillan/McGraw-Hill

At Home: Together, write three sentences about what happens to Matthew and Andrew.

Name_____

- The words *a, an,* and *the* are special adjectives called **articles**.
- Use *a* and *an* with singular nouns. Use *a* if the next word starts with a consonant sound.
- Use *an* if the next word starts with a vowel sound.
- Use *the* with singular nouns that name a particular person, place, or thing. Use *the* before all plural nouns.

Change the article in parentheses so that it correctly completes each sentence. Then rewrite the sentence on the line provided.

1. Matt's friends called him (an) hero.

   _____

2. They thought it was (a) unusual situation.

   _____

3. "That's (a) incredibly smart idea," said Randi.

   _____

4. On (a) first Monday of each month, all the students studied together.

   _____

   _____

5. Studying together with others means taking (a) time to listen and help.

   _____

   _____

6. Matt has (a) oak tree in his front yard.

   _____

7. Tom received (a) acceptance letter from the local college.

   _____

8. (A) earth's surface is seven parts water and three parts land.

   _____

   _____

At Home: Ask the student to write two more sentences using articles.

Name _____

- Use a colon to separate the hour and the minute in the time of day.
- Use a colon to introduce a list of items that ends a sentence.
- Use a colon after the greeting of a business letter.
- If there is no conjunction in a compound sentence, use a semicolon.

The writer of this letter didn't check for mistakes. Proofread the letter. Correct any colon, semicolon, or comma errors you find.

100 Decatur Avenue
North Platte NE 69101
April 13 2006

Dear Ms. Costello

    In an effort to streamline the hiring of new clerks for our library I tracked the number of library users from 800 A.M. on April 10 through 630 P.M. on April 12. My research indicates that we will need to hire at least two additional library clerks three might be advised. I have also ordered the following supplies new software for the computers refills for the laminating machines and paper for the copier.

    I look forward to hearing your decision on hiring.

Sincerely
Will O'Brien

At Home: Have the student write a letter listing tasks done by time. Have him or her use at least two colons and one semicolon in the letter.

Ta-Na-E-Ka • **Grade 6/Unit 5** 137

Name_____

- The words *a*, *an*, and *the* are special adjectives called **articles**.
- Use *a* and *an* with singular nouns.
- Use *a* if the next word starts with a consonant sound.
- Use *an* if the next word starts with a vowel sound.
- Use *the* with singular nouns that name a particular person, place, or thing.
- Use *the* before all plural nouns.

The writer of this compare/contrast essay did not proofread for mistakes. Put brackets [ ] around any incorrect use of articles. Add the correct punctuation and capitalization.

    Lily and Rose are an set of identical twins. But they are not identical in every way. Lily is an dreamer always late and often unprepared. She sleeps late every day and usually misses an school bus. Lily gets to class late often without an homework assignment.

    Rose however likes to be on time. She resets her alarm clock each night. Before bed, which is at 900 P.M., Rose lays out a outfit and packs her backpack with a books and homework she'll need a next day. Rose is usually calm and happy Lily tends to be anxious and scattered.

At Home: Have the student write an essay about a pair of twins. Remind him or her to use articles and punctuation correctly.

© Macmillan/McGraw-Hill

Put brackets [ ] around the correct article in the following sentences.

1. (A, An) study group formed at the middle school early last fall.

2. Keeping five sixth-grade students quiet is not (a, an) easy job.

3. (The, A) group meets every Monday at three o'clock.

4. (A, An) astonished librarian agreed to monitor their progress.

5. After a long day at school, (a, the) students still have a lot of energy.

6. They work on (a, an) different subject each week.

7. Last Monday, they agreed to work with (an, the) history textbook.

8. Some students wanted to use (the, an) computers available in the library.

9. There was (a, an) new computer sitting right on a nearby table.

10. (A, An) eager student used the computer to do his research on the Internet.

11. (A, The) more muscles are used, the larger and stronger they become.

12. When you cut (a, an) onion, it can make your eyes burn and water.

- The words *a, an,* and *the* are special adjectives called **articles**.
- Use *a* and *an* with singular nouns. Use *a* if the next word starts with a consonant sound.
- Use *an* if the next word starts with a vowel sound.
- Use *the* with singular nouns that name a particular person, place, or thing. Use *the* before all plural nouns.

Mechanics

- Use a colon to separate the hour and the minute in the time of day.
- Use a colon to introduce a list of items that ends a sentence.
- Use a colon after the greeting of a business letter.
- If there is no conjunction in a compound sentence, use a semicolon.

The writer of this letter didn't check for mistakes. As you read the letter, correct any colon errors you find. Put brackets [ ] around any incorrect use of articles.

100 Sherman Boulevard
Bangor, ME 04401
November 2, 2006

Dear Mr. Shen

Thank you so much for agreeing to pick me up at a Sarasota airport. My plane flight arrives at 817 A.M. on November 22, 2006. I am looking forward to being a part of an great Bird Counting Day on Thanksgiving! To prepare, I have made arrangements to have the following equipment sturdy walking shoes, binoculars, sunscreen, sunglasses, insect repellent, and an notebook for recording numbers and types of birds.

I am looking forward to working with an team I hope to be a good counter.

Sincerely,
Lydia Tallchief

Name_____

> - Adjectives are words that describe nouns.
> - The **comparative** form of an adjective compares two nouns.
> - Add -er to most one-syllable and some two-syllable adjectives to form the comparative.

Write the comparing forms of the following adjectives.

1. Bill is fast, but Morgan is _____ than Bill. (fast)

2. The grocery store is close, but the deli is _____. (close)

3. Our cat is proud, but our dog is _____. (proud)

4. This week is _____ than last week. (cold)

5. The upstairs bedroom is _____ than the downstairs living room. (warm)

Complete each sentence with the correct comparative form of the adjective in parentheses.

6. Alessandra wanted the (old) of the two coins for her collection.

   _____

7. Her collection is (large) than any I've seen.

   _____

8. She showed me one of the (new) coins in her collection.

   _____

9. It is (shiny) than this one.

   _____

10. Alessandra wants to build her collection (fast) than her brother.

    _____

At Home: Have the student make a list of five adjectives.

Grammar

Name_____

- The **comparative** form of an adjective compares two nouns.
- The **superlative** form compares more than two nouns.
- Add *-er* or *-est* to most one-syllable and some two-syllable adjectives to form the comparative and superlative.
- For adjectives ending in *e*, drop the *e* before adding *-er* or *-est*.
- For adjectives ending in a consonant and *y*, change *y* to *i* and add *-er* and *-est*.
- For one-syllable adjectives that have a single vowel before a final consonant, double the final consonant before adding *-er* or *-est*.

Complete each sentence with the correct comparative or superlative form of the adjective in parentheses. On the line after the sentence, write the correct form of another adjective that also makes sense in the sentence.

1. Theo is the (young) _____ member of the group.

   _____

2. It was the (busy) _____ group he had ever joined.

   _____

3. Their leader was the (happy) _____ woman Theo knew.

   _____

4. She was also the (wise) _____ person he had ever met.

   _____

5. It was (hot) _____ today than it was yesterday.

   _____

6. This building is (tall) _____ than that one.

   _____

At Home: Have the student choose four of the adjectives above and write sentences with them.

© Macmillan/McGraw-Hill

Name_____

- Compound nouns may be written as one word (*lifestyle, leftover, homework*), two separate words (*home page, box seat, paper clip*) or with a hyphen (*self-confidence, mother-in-law*). If you are unsure whether a compound noun is written as one word, two words, or hyphenated, consult your dictionary.
- Use a hyphen with compound numbers from twenty-one through ninety-nine.
- Use a hyphen with fractions used as modifiers, as in a *two-thirds* majority.
- Use a hyphen with the prefixes *ex-*, *self-*, and *all-*; with the suffix *-elect*.
- Use a hyphen with all prefixes before a proper noun or proper adjective.
- Hyphenate a compound adjective when it precedes the word it modifies: a *third-floor* office. Do not use a hyphen if one of the modifiers is an adverb ending in *-ly*: *freshly made bread*.

Read each sentence. Decide if the words in parentheses should be one, two words, or a hyphenated word. Write the word correctly on the line provided. If the words are correct, write C on the line. Consult your dictionary, if necessary.

1. We need to buy some (bird seed). _____

2. There is a (bird's nest) in the tree. _____

3. This is an (allEuropean) rowing team. _____

4. Is the (box office) open? _____

5. This is a (newly-hatched) egg. _____

6. I have (thirty two) marbles. _____

7. Use (one half) cup of sugar in the cake. _____

8. She is an (allstar) basketball player. _____

9. You need to have more (selfcontrol). _____

10. This is my sister's (boy-friend). _____

At Home: Have the student list two of each of the following: one-word, two-word, and hyphenated compound words.

Many Countries, One Currency:
Europe and the Euro • Grade 6/Unit 5

143

Name_____

- The **comparative** form of an adjective compares two nouns.
- The **superlative** form compares more than two nouns.

Proofread the point-of-view essay below for any errors in the use of comparative and superlative adjectives, punctuation, or capitalization.

    i have been asked to comment on the fast most economical way our club can bring aid to hungry children. we could collect nonperishable food. Collecting, packing, and shipping the food would be difficult, however? Who would distribute it! How would the children receive it.

    A smartest solution I believe is to collect money. Money is easy to collect easy to send overseas and easy for relief agencies, like the red cross, to put to good use. With money, agencies can buy food medicine or clothing--- whatever is needed. If I had to choose between sending food or sending money money is the smartest choice.

_____

_____

_____

_____

_____

_____

_____

_____

_____

_____

_____

_____

 At Home: Invite the student to write a point-of-view essay on a topic of his or her choice.

Name_____

Choose the correct replacement for the adjective form. Circle the letter of your answer.

1. Sari arrived (early) at the meeting than Bud.
   a. earliest
   b. earlier
   c. earlyer
   d. earlyest

2. The members had to choose the (fast) way to raise money.
   a. fastiest
   b. fastier
   c. faster
   d. fastest

3. Who was the (sleepy) member, Sari or Bud?
   a. sleepyest
   b. sleepiest
   c. sleepier
   d. sleepyer

Circle the letter of the correction that should be made to the following sentences.

4. Bud was the lazy member of the club.
   a. Change *member* to *members*.
   b. Change *lazy* to *lazier*.
   c. Change *lazy* to *laziest*.
   d. Change *was* to *were*.

5. Sari may be the angry member of the club.
   a. Change *angry* to *angriest*.
   b. Change *the* to *a*.
   c. Change *angry* to *angrier*.
   d. Change *may* to *was*.

6. Who do you think is nicest, Sari or Bud?
   a. Change *or* to *and*.
   b. Change *nicest* to *nicer*.
   c. Change *think* to *thinks*.
   d. Change *is* to *are*.

Name_____

- The **comparative** form of an adjective compares two nouns.
- The **superlative** form compares more than two nouns.

Mechanics

- Add *-er* or *-est* to most one-syllable and some two-syllable adjectives to form the comparative and superlative. For adjectives ending in *e*, drop the *e* before adding *-er* or *-est*. For adjectives ending in a consonant and *y*, change *y* to *i* and add *-er* and *-est*. For one-syllable adjectives that have a single vowel before a final consonant, double the final consonant before adding *-er* or *-est*.
- Use a hyphen with compound numbers from twenty-one through ninety-nine; with fractions used as modifiers, as in a *two-thirds* majority; with the prefixes *ex-*, *self-*, and *all-*; with the suffix *-elect*; with all prefixes before a proper noun or proper adjective.
- Hyphenate a compound adjective when it precedes the word it modifies: a *third-floor* office. Do not use a hyphen if one of the modifiers is an adverb ending in *-ly*: *freshly made bread*.

Rewrite the sentences that describe the picture. Use the correct comparative or superlative form of the adjective. Make sure hyphens are used correctly.

1. Sari can count fast than Bud.

_____

2. Bud has already been counting coins for one half hour.

_____

3. Sari and Bud would like some freshly-baked cookies.

_____

4. Bud is the hungry boy Sari has ever met.

_____

© Macmillan/McGraw-Hill

- For most adjectives with two or more syllables, use *more* to form the comparative.

Put brackets [ ] around the word or words in parentheses that form a correct comparative adjective.

1. Justin's baseball card collection is (more extensive, extensiver than mine.

2. Do you find old basketball cards (difficulter, more difficult) to find than baseball cards?

3. Mr. Smythe was (patienter, more patient) than usual when we were looking for new cards in his shop.

4. Justin thinks a Babe Ruth card is (more expensive, expensiver) than his parents' car.

5. Justin's method of categorizing cards is (more intricate, intricater) than mine.

6. Which card shop is (nearer, more near) to my house?

7. Of the two collections, Justin's was the (more fun, funner).

8. The shortstop on the team seems (tougher, more tough) than the catcher.

9. That game, at eighteen innings, was (intensest, more intense) than the one I saw last month.

10. Who is (more friendly, friendlier), the pitcher or the goalie?

At Home: Have the student find and underline comparative and superlative adjectives in a newspaper or magazine article.

Honus and Me • Grade 6/Unit 5 147

© Macmillan/McGraw-Hill

Name_____

- Never use *more* or *most* with the *-er* or *-est* form of an adjective.

On the line provided, write the comparative or superlative adjective that correctly completes each sentence.

1. Hannah has the (most amazing, amazingest) collection of bells.

   _____

2. She claims to choose only the (most pretty, prettiest) bells.

   _____

3. I've noticed that the sound of Hannah's bells is (more pleasing, pleasinger) than most.

   _____

4. The clear peal of each bell is (most satisfying, satisfyingest).

   _____

5. Hannah's collection of bells is the (largest, most large) I've ever seen.

   _____

6. The sound of this bell is (more deep, deeper) than the sound of that one.

   _____

7. This little bell has the (sweetest, most sweet) sound of all.

   _____

8. When we ring Hannah's bells all at once, the house is the (most noisy, noisiest) it's ever been.

   _____

9. Diana is (more eager, eagerer) than Tasha to start a bell collection.

   _____

10. Diana probably will get her first bell (more soon, sooner) than Tasha.

    _____

At Home: Have the student choose five of the adjectives above and write sentences using them.

- For most adjectives with two or more syllables, use *more* to form the comparative.
- For most adjectives with two or more syllables, use *most* to form the superlative.
- Never use *more* or *most* with the *-er* or *-est* form of an adjective.

The writer of the following paragraph did not check his or her use of adjectives. Rewrite the paragraph, making sure that comparative and superlative adjectives are used correctly.

Hannah and Natalie like to debate whose collection is the interestinger. Hannah has the bigger collection of bells I've ever seen. She has at least two hundred bells! Natalie collects the beautifulest seashells. Her seashells are really amazing!

Hannah and Natalie don't know it yet, but my collection of state flags is the incrediblest collection of all. I have collected flags from every state except Alaska. I am eagerest to get the Alaska state flag, but it has proved to be the difficultest to get.

_____

_____

_____

_____

_____

_____

_____

_____

_____

© Macmillan/McGraw-Hill

At Home: Have the student underline the words and phrases that help in figuring out each word's meaning.

Name_____

- For most adjectives with two or more syllables, use *more* to form the comparative.
- For most adjectives with two or more syllables, use *most* to form the superlative.

Mechanics

- Never use *more* or *most* with the *-er* or *-est* form of an adjective.
- Each line of a poem usually begins with a capital letter.

Put brackets [ ] around any comparative or superlative adjectives. Correct any mistakes in adjective use. Then rewrite the poems, using correct punctuation.

three wise men of Gotham
went to sea in a bowl.
If the bowl had been stronger
my song would have been longer.

my bells sing so sweetly,
most sweetly than yours.
my bells look so lovely,
the lovelier of all.

_____
_____
_____
_____
_____
_____
_____
_____

© Macmillan/McGraw-Hill

Name _____

Put brackets [ ] around the word or words that form a comparative or superlative adjective. Write a *C* if the adjective is comparative. Write an *S* if the adjective is superlative.

1. Natalie's collection of seashells is the most stunning I've ever seen.

    _____

2. The lightning whelk is Natalie's most unusual shell. _____

3. Natalie's collection is larger than mine. _____

4. My most valuable shell is a moon snail. _____

5. Natalie's horse conch is the more colorful of the two. _____

Choose the comparative or superlative form of the adjective in parentheses that correctly completes the sentence. Write your answer on the line provided.

6. The longer Natalie picked up shells, the (full) _____ her pail became.

7. The (unusual) _____ shell Natalie found was a lace murex.

8. A kitten's paw shell is much (small) _____ than a lion's paw shell.

9. The (tiny) _____ shell of all in Natalie's collection is the zigzag scallop.

10. A true tulip shell is much (long) _____ than a banded tulip.

Name_____

- For most adjectives with two or more syllables, use *more* to form the comparative.
- For most adjectives with two or more syllables, use *most* to form the superlative.
- Never use *more* or *most* with the *-er* or *-est* form of an adjective.

Complete each sentence with the correct form of *more* or *most*.

1. Natalie has the _____ exquisite sample of a lightning whelk I've ever seen.

2. The angel wing is the _____ challenging shell to find in Florida.

3. Natalie claims that I have been the _____ successful beachcomber.

4. But I think that Jason has been _____ successful than I.

5. He managed to find the _____ unusual shell, the Sunray Venus.

Name_____

- The comparative form of *good* is *better*.
- The superlative form of *good* is *best*.

Rewrite each sentence, using the correct comparative or superlative form of the adjective in parentheses.

1. Sometimes the (goodest, best) thing to do is to stand up for what is right.

   _____

   _____

2. Juan's father, Jacob, wanted to get a (gooder, better) job.

   _____

3. He also wanted (gooder, better) working conditions for the people on his crew.

   _____

   _____

4. Jacob chose the (goodest, best) time to state his case.

   _____

5. He knew there was a (better, gooder) way to manage the business.

   _____

Put brackets[ ]around the comparative or superlative form of the adjective in each sentence. In the blank, write *C* if it is a comparative or *S* if it is a superlative adjective.

6. Did Jacob manage to secure better working conditions? _____

7. He wants the best possible work environment for everyone. _____

8. The other workers agree that Jacob is the best speaker in their group.

   _____

9. They all want a better life. _____

10. Jacob made the best presentation of all. _____

 At Home: Have the student write three sentences using good, better, and best as adjectives.

© Macmillan/McGraw-Hill

Name_____

- The comparative form of *bad* is *worse*.
- The superlative form of *bad* is *worst*.

On the blank provided, write the correct comparative or superlative form of the adjective in parentheses.

1. Juan decided that the food in the school cafeteria was (badder, worse) than ever. _____

2. Stevi said that their food was no (worser, worse) than any other school's food. _____

3. Juan stated that it was the (baddest, worst) in the county. _____

4. Which is (badder, worse), eating bad food or having to pay extra for it? _____

5. For Juan, the (baddest, worst) thing was having no fresh food at all. _____

6. "This is the (worst, baddest) example of nutrition I have ever seen," said Juan. _____

7. French fries every day are a (badder, worse) choice than a baked potato. _____

8. Soda is a (worse, badder) choice than fresh milk. _____

9. The (worst, baddest) thing, Juan decided, was that students were forming bad habits. _____

10. Juan noticed that the lunches were the (baddest, worst) on Fridays. _____

© Macmillan/McGraw-Hill

At Home: Ask the student to write four sentences using worse and worst in each sentence.

Name_____

Comparing with *Good*
- The comparative form of *good* is *better*.
- The superlative form of *good* is *best*.

Comparing with *Bad*
- The comparative form of *bad* is *worse*.
- The superlative form of *bad* is *worst*

Read the sentences below. Put brackets [ ] around any incorrect comparative or superlative adjectives. Rewrite the sentences on the lines provided. If the sentence is correct, write C.

1. "That was the baddest lunch I have ever eaten," said Juan.

_____

2. "What do you suggest for a better lunch?" asked Josie.

_____

3. "Some fresh vegetables would be a gooder start," said Juan.

_____

4. "Even gooder would be some whole grain bread for our sandwiches," he added.

_____

_____

5. "The worstest thing is that the students don't even know that the food is not good for them!" he exclaimed.

_____

_____

At Home: Ask the student to choose three adjectives from the sentences above and write sentences for each.

Let It Shine • Grade 6/Unit 5 155

© Macmillan/McGraw-Hill

Name_____

Comparing with *Good*
- The comparative form of *good* is *better*.
- The superlative form of *good* is *best*.

Comparing with *Bad*
- The comparative form of *bad* is *worse*.
- The superlative form of *bad* is *worst*

Correct any mistakes in punctuating the following eyewitness account. Make sure comparative and superlative adjectives are used correctly. Then rewrite the account.

When I entered JFK Middle School last fall I was appalled at the quality of the school lunches. Students were offered only the baddest in terms of healthful foods: processed foods, high in sugar, salt, and fat, and high-sugar sodas and candy from the vending machines. I knew there was a betterer way to eat. I formed a committee to investigate the problem and found a best way to bring only the most freshest food to our students. My committee was called "From Worse to Bests: How to Eat Right." Now we have much gooder choices in the school cafeteria.

_____

_____

_____

_____

_____

_____

_____

_____

_____

At Home: Invite the student to write an imaginary eyewitness account of an effort to make things better in some way at school.

Choose the best comparative or superlative form of *good*. Circle the letter of your choice.

1. Juan's lunch was the (good) of the two.
   a. better
   b. goodest
   c. best
   d. gooder

2. The school principal chose the (good) food company of the three he studied.
   a. gooder
   b. better
   c. best
   d. bestest

3. Josie likes broccoli (good) than cauliflower.
   a. bester
   b. gooder
   c. best
   d. better

Choose the best comparative or superlative form of *bad*. Circle the letter of your choice.

4. For one student, lunch was the (bad) meal of the day.
   a. worst
   b. badder
   c. baddest
   d. worse

5. Which is (bad) for lunch, candy or soda?
   a. worst
   b. badder
   c. worse
   d. baddest

6. French fries are (bad) for you than a baked potato.
   a. badder
   b. worst
   c. baddest
   d. worse

Name_____

> Comparing with *Good*
> - The comparative form of *good* is *better*.
> - The superlative form of *good* is *best*.
>
> Comparing with *Bad*
> - The comparative form of *bad* is *worse*.
> - The superlative form of *bad* is *worst*

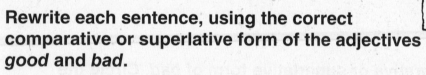

Rewrite each sentence, using the correct comparative or superlative form of the adjectives *good* and *bad*.

1. Juan is the (good) organizer at JFK Middle School.

_____

_____

2. He hopes for the (good) but plans for the (bad).

_____

_____

3. Because of Juan, we now have much (good) food to eat each day.

_____

_____

4. Nothing is (bad) than a greasy lunch.

_____

_____

Name_____

Read the passages below and look at each underlined section. Is there a mistake? If there is, how do you correct it? Circle the letter of your answer.

Josie and Juan made up a questionnaire for the students at school. The first

question was, "Which is gooder for dessert, apple sauce or chocolate candy?"
                            (1)

The second question was, "Which is nourishinger, grilled chicken or a cheeseburger?"
                                              (2)

The third question was, "Would you rather eat lunch at 1130 A.M. or noon?"
                         (3)

1. **A.** Change *gooder* to *better*.
   B. Add a comma after *sauce*.
   C. Change *Which* to *What*.
   D. No mistake

2. **A.** Change *is* to *are*.
   B. Change *nourishinger* to *more nourishing*.
   C. Change the question mark to a period.
   D. No mistake

3. **A.** Change *Would* to *Will*.
   B. Change *rather* to *want*.
   C. Change *1130 A.M.* to *11:30 A.M.*
   D. No mistake

Since Juan spoke the language fluently, he was asked to tutor students in
                     (4)

spanish class. Today, he reviewed thirty-one pages of grammar with Josie.
              (5)

4. **A.** Change *was* to *were*.
   B. Change *language* to *Language*.
   C. Change *spanish class* to *Spanish class*.
   D. No mistake

5. **A.** Change *reviewed* to *reviewing*.
   B. Change *thirty-one* to *thirty one*.
   C. Change *with Josie* to *to Josie*.
   D. No mistake

At Home: Ask the student to write one sentence using a proper adjective.

© Macmillan/McGraw-Hill

Name_____

Read the passages below and look at each underlined section. Is there a mistake? If there is, how do you correct it? Circle the letter of your answer.

Josie said, "Our success with school lunches is the amazingest thing I've ever

<u>(6)</u>

<u>been a part of!"</u> Lunchtime is so much <u>more pleasanter than it was before.</u> Our

<u>(7)</u>

school food is the <u>most fresh of any school around!"</u>

<u>(8)</u>

6. A. Change amazingest to most amazing.
   B. Add a comma after success.
   C. Change lunches to lunching.
   D. No mistake

7. A. Change so to as.
   B. Change much more pleasanter to much more pleasant.
   C. Change the than to that.
   D. No mistake

8. A. Change Our to Ours.
   B. Change any to that.
   C. Change most fresh to freshest.
   D. No mistake

Josie likes to <u>eat fruit she especially likes apples.</u> These are the <u>fruits available</u>

<u>(9)</u>

<u>today at school: apples, pears, bananas, grapes.</u>

<u>(10)</u>

9. A. Add a comma after fruit.
   B. Change fruit to Fruit.
   C. Add a semicolon after fruit.
   D. No mistake

10. A. Change are to was.
    B. Change These to This.
    C. Change the colon to a semicolon.
    D. No mistake

At Home: Ask the student to write three sentences using three different kinds of adjectives.

Name_____

• An **adverb** is a word that modifies a verb, an adjective, or another adverb.
• An adverb can tell how, when, or where an action takes place.

Put brackets [ ] around each adverb in the sentences below.

1. Tameesha hurriedly hopped on her bike.

2. She quickly pedaled to the fabric store.

3. She wanted to find the perfect fabric soon.

4. Tameesha eagerly looked through the bolts of material.

5. She was usually lucky at this store.

6. Today, she hoped to find some beautiful blue material.

7. Tameesha quickly grabbed the pale blue silk.

8. It was easily the most beautiful color!

9. Tameesha seldom found fabric so perfect.

10. She hugged the fabric happily.

11. The alarm clock went off at 7:00 A.M., and Tameesha instantly jumped out of bed.

12. The dog ran wildly after a squirrel that he saw in the park.

At Home: Have the student write three sentences about finding something perfect.

Leonardo's Horse • Grade 6/Unit 6 161

Name_____

- An **adverb** is a word that modifies a verb, an adjective, or another adverb.
- An **adverb** can tell how, when, or where an action takes place.
- **Adverbs** that modify adjectives and adverbs answer the questions *how?* and *to what extent?*
- When an adverb emphasizes or intensifies the meaning, it is called an **intensifier**. Some examples are *very, extremely, just, quite, rather, so, too,* and *somewhat.*

Read each sentence. Then put brackets [ ] around each adverb that describes an adjective or another adverb. Next, in the blank, write the adjective or adverb being modified. Write *I* after any sentence that contains an intensifier.

1. Tameesha could sew quite well. _____

2. Her dresses were designed very classically. _____

3. "I feel completely happy when I am designing," Tameesha has said.

   _____

4. Her newest design was exceptionally fine. _____

5. Tameesha's designs are not overly dramatic. _____

6. But the dresses, shirts, and pants are always surprising.

   _____

7. Tameesha does not use very costly materials. _____

8. "Her designs are surprisingly simple," said Mr. Lewis. _____

9. Tameesha was suddenly silent when she heard that statement.

   _____

10. "I prefer to say that my clothing designs are simply classic," she

    answered. _____

At Home: Have the student write a sentence using three of the adverbs above to modify an adjective or another adverb.

Name_____

- *Good* is an adjective and is used to describe nouns.
- *Well* is an adverb that tells *how* about a verb.
- When *well* means "healthy," it is used as an adjective.

Read each sentence. Then fill in the blank using *good* or *well* correctly.

1. Tameesha's grandmother bought her a _____ used sewing machine.

2. She learned the basics of sewing _____ and soon was making aprons and napkins.

3. You can _____ imagine Tameesha's talent, as she was only seven years old!

4. Her grandmother has taught her _____.

5. Tameesha's sister did not learn the basics of sewing _____.

6. She did not think it was a _____ idea to start making aprons and napkins.

7. But Tameesha wanted to do everything _____.

8. She found a _____ place to store her fabrics and thread.

9. "Are you feeling _____?" Tameesha asked her grandmother.

10. "I can see you are feeling very _____ about yourself!" said Gran.

© Macmillan/McGraw-Hill

At Home: Have the student write four sentences, two using *good* and two using *well* correctly.

Leonardo's Horse • Grade 6/Unit 6   **163**

Name_____

- An **adverb** is a word that modifies a verb, an adjective, or another adverb.
- An **adverb** can tell how, when, or where an action takes place.
- **Adverbs** that modify adjectives and adverbs answer the questions *how?* and *to what extent?*

Mechanics

- *Good* is an adjective and is used to describe nouns.
- *Well* is an adverb that tells *how* about a verb.
- When *well* means "healthy," it is used as an adjective.

Correct any errors in the use of adverbs, and in the use of *good* and *well* in the directions below. Then rewrite the directions, correcting any errors in the use of adverbs, capitalization, or punctuation. Some sentences may be correct as is.

Tameesha quickly wrote these directions for making a simple A-line dress.

1. First, careful choose a pattern for your appropriate body type. Purchase from a well company.

2. Then buy the fabric. Don't buy very costly fabric for your first project.

3. Always read the pattern directions slow.

4. Careful cut out the pattern pieces.

_____
_____
_____
_____
_____
_____

Name

Put brackets [ ] around the adverb in each of the following sentences. Write *how* if the adverbs tell how, *when* if the adverbs tells when, or *where* if the adverb tell where the action takes place.

1. Tameesha thought her prom gown draped beautifully. _____

2. She wanted to wear it immediately. _____

3. Her grandmother said, "You cannot wear it now!" _____

4. So Tameesha put the gown away. _____

5. She carefully hung it on a padded hanger in her closet.

   _____

Put brackets around the adverb in each of the following sentences. On the line provided, write the word the adverb modifies.

6. Tameesha's confidence in her designs grew steadily. _____

7. She quite readily purchased difficult patterns. _____

8. Tameesha finally realized she did not need to buy patterns.

   _____

9. She often sketched her own designs. _____

10. Tameesha finally thought of herself as a classic designer.

    _____

Name_____

- An **adverb** is a word that modifies a verb, an adjective, or another adverb.
- An **adverb** can tell how, when, or where an action takes place.
- **Adverbs** that modify adjectives and adverbs answer the questions *how?* and *to what extent?*

Put brackets [ ] around the adverbs in the following sentences. Write *how* if the adverb tells how, *when* if the adverb tells when, or *where* if the adverb tells where the action takes place.

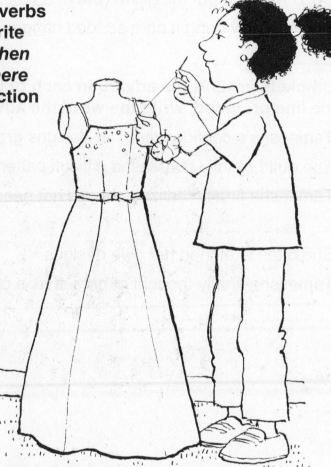

1. Tameesha easily draped the silk over the mannequin. _____

2. She sometimes asked her grandmother for help. _____

3. But Tameesha usually figured things out for herself. _____

4. She picked up her needle and began to sew. _____

5. Tameesha knew she seldom made a mistake. _____

- The **comparative** form of an adverb compares two actions.
- The **superlative** form of an adverb compares more than two actions.
- For all one-syllable and some two-syllable adverbs, add *-er* and *-est* to form the comparative or superlative.

Write the comparative and superlative form of each of the following adverbs.

	Comparative	Superlative
1. fast	_____	_____
2. high	_____	_____
3. loud	_____	_____
4. long	_____	_____
5. near	_____	_____

Write each sentence using the comparative or superlative form of the following adverbs in parentheses.

6. Andre read the book about time travel (fast) than Thomas did.

_____

_____

7. Andre went to bed (soon) than Thomas.

_____

8. Thomas said, "I want to jump (high) of all."

_____

9. Andre is the (fast) runner on the team.

_____

10. Thomas wants to jump (high) than Andre.

_____

At Home: Have the student write three sentences comparing Andre and Thomas and other members of the track team.

- For adverbs that end in *-ly* and most other adverbs with two or more syllables, use *more* to form the comparative and *most* to form the superlative.
- When you use *more* or *most*, do not use the ending *-er* or *-est*.

Write the comparative or superlative forms of each of the following adverbs.

	Comparative	Superlative
1. suddenly		
2. frequently		
3. widely		
4. naturally		
5. weakly		

Each sentence below contains an incorrectly formed adverb in parentheses. Put brackets [ ] around the correct adverb.

6. Andre traveled (most comfortably, more comfortably) in the time machine than Thomas.

7. Andre slept (more soundly, most soundly) of all the boys.

8. Thomas said, "My flashlight shines (most radiantly, radiantlier) of all.

9. Andre sings (more naturally, most naturally) than Thomas.

10. Thomas sang (most forcefully, more forcefully) of all.

© Macmillan/McGraw-Hill

- Some adverbs have irregular forms.
- The comparative and superlative forms of *well* are *better* and *best*.
- The comparative and superlative forms of *badly* are *worse* and *worst*.
- Never use *more* or *most* with irregular forms.

Rewrite each sentence below by writing the correct comparative form of the adverb shown in parentheses.

1. The Time Travel Club meeting in January was (well) attended than the one in December.

_____

_____

2. Andre's presentation at the Time Travel Club meeting was (well) than Hannah's.

_____

_____

3. The hurricane in August affected attendance (badly) than last year's storm.

_____

_____

Rewrite each sentence below by writing the correct superlative form of the adverb shown in parentheses.

4. The MLK Middle School Time Travel Club is the (well) known of all the clubs in the county.

_____

_____

5. Everyone agrees that Andre can be the (badly) behaved member of the club.

_____

_____

© Macmillan/McGraw-Hill

At Home: Have the student write four more sentences using the comparative and superlative forms of *well* and *badly*.

Name_____

- The **comparative** form of an adverb compares two actions.
- The **superlative** form of an adverb compares more than two actions.

Correct any errors in the use of comparative and superlative adverbs, and in the use of *well* and *badly* in the directions below. Then rewrite the explanatory essay, correcting any errors in the use of adverbs, capitalization, or punctuation.

You do not need to reason most brilliantly than Albert Einstein in order to well understand the dimension of time. Many people most incorrect believe that time is a constant, and that we are moving eagerlier through time at a fixed rate. But you can perform a well-known experiment to show that time is not constant. Try sitting through a boring movie. Does time move quicklyer? Then think about a ride on a rollercoaster. Does time move fastest then? There is no easy explanation for why time moves more quickly sometimes and more slowly at other times. It's just a fact of life.

_____

_____

_____

_____

_____

_____

_____

_____

_____

© Macmillan/McGraw-Hill

At Home: Have the student write an explanatory essay on a topic of his or her choice. Remind him or her to use adverbs correctly when writing.

Read each of the following sentences. Is there a mistake with the comparative adverb? Circle the letter of your response.

1. Thomas jumped highly than he ever had before.

   a. Change *highly* to *higher*.

   b. Change *highly* to *highlier*.

   c. Change *highly* to *more higher*.

   d. Make no change.

2. Andre felt gooder after he made his presentation.

   a. Change *gooder* to *bester*.

   b. Change *gooder* to *more good*.

   c. Change *gooder* to *better*.

   d. Make no change.

3. The sun shines more brightly at noon than at dusk.

   a. Change *more* to *most*.

   b. Change *brightly* to *brighter*.

   c. Change more *brightly* to *brightlier*.

   d. Make no change.

Read each of the following sentences. Is there a mistake with the superlative adverb? Circle the letter of your response.

4. Thomas sauntered casuallyier to the podium and waited.

   a. Change *casuallyier* to *most casually*.

   b. Change *casuallyier* to *casualiest*.

   c. Change *casuallyier* to *more casuallyier*.

   d. Make no change.

5. Andre has the worst behavior of all the students in class.

   a. Change *worst* to *worse*.

   b. Change *worst* to *badliest*.

   c. Change *worst* to *better*.

   d. Make no change.

Name_____

- The **comparative** form of an adverb compares two actions.
- The **superlative** form of an adverb compares more than two actions.
- For all one-syllable and some two-syllable adverbs, add -*er* and -*est* to form the comparative or superlative.
- For adverbs that end in -*ly* and most other adverbs with two or more syllables, use *more* to form the comparative and *most* to form the superlative.
- When you use *more* or *most*, do not use the ending -*er* or -*est*.
- Some adverbs have irregular forms. The comparative and superlative forms of *well* are *better* and *best*. The comparative and superlative forms of *badly* are *worse* and *worst*.
- **Never use** *more* **or** *most* **with irregular forms.**

**Read each sentence aloud. Choose the correct
comparative or superlative adverb in parentheses.
Write the sentence on the line provided.**

1. Andre thinks (clearliest, more clearly)
   after a healthy breakfast.

   _____

   _____

2. Andre made his presentation
   (most perfectly, perfectest).

   _____

   _____

3. He thinks (highlier, more highly) of your speech than mine.

   _____

4. Andre's bicycle runs (most smoothly, smoothliest) right after its tune-up.

   _____

   _____

Name_____

- A **negative** is a word that means "no," such as *not*, *never*, *nobody*, *nowhere*, and contractions with *n't*.
- A **double negative** is an error in which two negatives are used together.
- You can correct a double negative by removing one negative.

Put brackets [ ] around each negative in the sentences below.

1. Lupe did not think Spanish would be difficult to master.

2. Lupe's grandparents no longer spoke it around the house.

3. In fact, nobody in Lupe's family spoke Spanish anymore.

4. Lupe never thought she would miss hearing it.

5. "Why can't I sign up for Spanish?" Lupe asked her teacher.

Each sentence below contains a double negative. Put brackets [ ] around the negative words and correctly rewrite the sentence by removing one negative.

6. "No student cannot sign up for a language after September fifth," said Ms. Garcia.

   _____

   _____

7. The language teachers could not allow no more students into the classes.

   _____

   _____

8. Lupe didn't not know what to do.

   _____

9. She could not ask no teacher to help her.

   _____

10. She might not never learn to speak Spanish.

    _____

© Macmillan/McGraw-Hill

At Home: Have the student create five sentences containing double negatives, and then correct them.

These Walls Can Talk **173**
Grade 6/Unit 6

Name_____

> • You can correct a double negative by replacing one negative with a positive word.

Read each sentence. If the sentence contains a double negative, rewrite it correctly. If the sentence is correct, write C on the line provided.

1. Lupe decided to ask her grandfather for help, not her grandmother.

   _____

   _____

2. Lupe's grandfather, Oswaldo, wasn't no easy teacher.

   _____

   _____

3. But Lupe knew she wouldn't never find a better person to teach her Spanish.

   _____

   _____

4. Most grandparents didn't never get the opportunity to teach their grandchildren.

   _____

   _____

5. Oswaldo was not going to miss it!

   _____

   _____

6. Oswaldo wasn't sorry he studied Spanish.

   _____

   _____

© Macmillan/McGraw-Hill

At Home: Have the student identify the positive words in his or her corrected sentences.

Name_____

- A **negative** is a word that means "no," such as *not*, *never*, *nobody*, *nowhere*, and contractions with *n't*.
- A **double negative** is an error in which two negatives are used together.
- You can correct a double negative by removing one negative.
- You can correct a double negative by replacing one negative with a positive word.

Rewrite each sentence below on the line provided so that it does not contain a double negative.

1. Oswaldo would never let no one read his Spanish novels.

_____

_____

2. No person in the house couldn't touch his books.

_____

_____

3. Oswaldo knew nobody had no ability to read his Spanish books.

_____

_____

4. Lupe had never encountered no person like her grandfather.

_____

_____

5. Without Oswaldo, Lupe wouldn't never have learned Spanish.

_____

_____

© Macmillan/McGraw-Hill

At Home: Have the student write five sentences with one negative word in each.

These Walls Can Talk
Grade 6/Unit 6
175

Name_____

- A **negative** is a word that means "no," such as *not*, *never*, *nobody*, *nowhere*, and contractions with *n't*.
- A **double negative** is an error in which two negatives are used together.
- You can correct a double negative by removing one negative.
- You can correct a double negative by replacing one negative with a positive word.

Proofread the persuasive editorial below for errors in the use of negatives, punctuation, or capitalization. Then rewrite the editorial.

As president of the school council, I have been asked to comment on the efforts by a group of students to take down the class photos in the corridor outside principal hernandez's Office. These photos show graduates of cleveland middle school for the last twenty five years. The students who don't believe these class photos should not be replaced with decorative posters don't not understand that our past is a part of us. I strongly urge students to keep in touch with the present and future by not preserving our reminders of the past.

_____

_____

_____

_____

_____

_____

_____

_____

At Home: Invite the student to write a persuasive essay on a topic of his or her choice.

Each sentence below contains a double negative. Rewrite the sentence correctly on the line provided.

1. The students didn't have no respect for the past.

   _____

2. Not no person in the school realized the importance of the class photos.

   _____

   _____

3. No one nowhere in this school was willing to speak up.

   _____

4. It didn't take no time for our student council president to act.

   _____

5. She wouldn't not miss the opportunity to write about it.

   _____

   _____

6. There wasn't no reason to stay silent.

   _____

7. No student did not want to miss her editorial.

   _____

8. The students looked for a mistake but couldn't find none.

   _____

   _____

9. They didn't have nothing to complain about.

   _____

10. They hadn't never voted on such an issue before.

    _____

Name_____

> • A **negative** is a word that means "no," such as *not*, *never*,
>   *nobody*, *nowhere*, and contractions with *n't*.
> • A **double negative** is an error in which two negatives are used
>   together.
> • You can correct a double negative by removing one negative.
> • You can correct a double negative by replacing one negative
>   with a positive word.

**Rewrite each sentence on the line provided,
correcting the double negatives.**

1. Lupe was not no complainer.

_____

_____

2. Lupe didn't not become president to stay quiet.

_____

_____

3. She wasn't no activist, but Lupe was eager to make the school better.

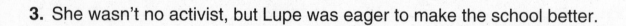

_____

4. Lupe said there wasn't no reason not to fight for what we want.

_____

_____

- A **preposition** comes before a noun or pronoun and relates that noun or pronoun to another word in the sentence.
- Common prepositions are *about, above, across, after, around, at, before, behind, below, between, beyond, down, for, from, in, near, of, on, over, to, with.*

Put brackets [ ] around the prepositions in each sentence. Some sentences have more than one preposition.

1. Ashley liked to help her dad in his newspaper business.
2. On Sunday mornings, Ashley and Mr. Peters got up early.
3. They drove to the offices of *The Asheville Journal*.
4. There, Mr. Peters got the Sunday editions of the paper.
5. Ashley put each newspaper into a plastic bag to keep it from getting wet.
6. Then, after putting the papers in the back of the truck, they left.
7. Ashley sat in the backseat between piles of papers.
8. She enjoyed this time with her father on his route.
9. Mr. Peters threw the newspaper across the lawn.
10. The paper landed near the front door.
11. As she looked beyond the horizon, she could see that a severe thunderstorm was coming her way.
12. On the long bus ride home, Jennifer sat behind a cranky baby.
13. A baby bird gets its food from its mother until it can leave the nest and fly on its own.
14. A flock of geese flew over the school today.

© Macmillan/McGraw-Hill

At Home: Have the student write three sentences using six different prepositions.

Name_____

- A **prepositional phrase** is a group of words that begins with a preposition and ends with a noun or pronoun.
- The **object of a preposition** is the noun or pronoun that follows the preposition.
- The verb must agree with the subject, not with the object of the preposition.

Read each sentence below. Underline each prepositional phrase, and put brackets [ ] around the object of the preposition. One sentence has two prepositional phrases.

1. Ashley found herself becoming interested in the newspaper business.

2. She asked her teacher to recommend books about journalism.

3. Ashley's teacher gave her a list with several titles.

4. Ashley selected one of the books from the school library.

5. She put the book into her backpack.

Each sentence below contains an incorrectly formed adverb in parentheses. Put brackets [ ] around the correct adverb.

6. The book in the backpack (belongs, belong) to Ashley.

_____

7. The book in the backseat of the car (needs, need) to be returned.

_____

8. The rules of the library (is, are) important.

_____

9. Ashley's neighbors across the street (were, was) journalists.

_____

10. Their articles in the newspaper (was, were) fascinating.

_____

At Home: Have the student circle the prepositions in the sentences above.

© Macmillan/McGraw-Hill

Name_____

- Use a comma after an introductory word, such as *well*.
- Use commas to set off words that interrupt the flow of thought.
- Use commas to set off nouns of direct address and most appositives.
- Use a comma after a long introductory prepositional phrase.

On the lines provided, rewrite the sentences by inserting commas in the appropriate places.

1. "Well I think it would be fascinating to be a journalist," said Ashley.

_____

_____

2. "Dad look at this article in the paper about journalism camp," said Ashley.

_____

_____

3. After two weeks of journalism camp Ashley felt she had learned a lot.

_____

_____

4. The Truman Institute which is located in Asheville offered writing classes, too.

_____

_____

5. "Sir may I introduce my father Mr. Peters?" said Ashley.

_____

_____

6. "So what do you want to study Ashley?" asked Mrs. Rivers.

_____

_____

© Macmillan/McGraw-Hill

At Home: Have the student write a sentence for each of the guidelines in the box above.

Breaking into Print • Grade 6/Unit 6   181

Name_____

- A **preposition** comes before a noun or pronoun and relates that noun or pronoun to another word in the sentence.
- Common prepositions are *about, above, across, after, around, at, before, behind, below, between, down, for, from, in, near, of, on, over, to, with*.
- A **prepositional phrase** is a group of words that begins with a preposition and ends with a noun or pronoun.
- The **object of a preposition** is the noun or pronoun that follows the preposition.
- The verb must agree with the subject, not with the object of the preposition.

Read the following explanation of a process. Correct any mistakes in the use of prepositions, prepositional phrases, capitalization, or punctuation. Then rewrite the explanation.

   The process of writing and publishing a book have changed dramatically in the past fifteen years. Before the advent of computers, writers needed publishing companies to print bind and distribute their books. Now it can all be done electronically. First, write your story. Then read through your rough draft which is also called a first pass. When you are sure your story is as good as it can be create your own website and become your own publisher!

_____

_____

_____

_____

_____

_____

_____

_____

© Macmillan/McGraw-Hill

At Home: Invite the student to write a short explanation of a process, using at least three prepositions.

Identify the object of the preposition in each of the following sentences. Circle the letter of your choice.

1. Ashley and her father arrived home from work.
   a. and
   b. father
   c. from
   d. work

2. Ashley's bedroom was across the hall.
   a. bedroom
   b. was
   c. hall
   d. across

3. Ashley put her journalism books in the new bookcase.
   a. bookcase
   b. put
   c. new
   d. in

Read each of the following sentences. Is there a mistake? Circle the letter of your response.

4. Around five o'clock Ashley's father called her for dinner.
   a. Add a comma after o'clock.
   b. Change Ashley's to Ashleys'
   c. Change calls to call
   d. Correct

5. Ashley, of course, washed her hands and went right into the kitchen.
   a. Change washed to washing.
   b. Take away the comma after Ashley.
   c. Add a comma after right.
   d. Correct

Name _____

- A **preposition** comes before a noun or pronoun and relates that noun or pronoun to another word in the sentence.
- Common prepositions are *about, above, across, after, around, at, before, behind, below, between, down, for, from, in, near, of, on, over, to, with.*
- A **prepositional phrase** is a group of words that begins with a preposition and ends with a noun or pronoun.
- The **object of a preposition** is the noun or pronoun that follows the preposition.
- The verb must agree with the subject, not with the object of the preposition.

Read each sentence aloud. Then change the verb so that it agrees with the subject of the sentence. Rewrite each sentence on the line provided. Then add commas after prepositional phrases if they are necessary.

1. At journalism camp the class write articles for the camp newspaper.

   _____

   _____

2. Between journalism classes and helping her father Ashley have little free time.

   _____

   _____

3. A number of students attends Ashley's journalism classes.

   _____

   _____

4. Around the corner from where Ashley attends camp her father work in a newspaper office.

   _____

   _____

Name_____

> • Two sentences can be combined by adding an adjective or adverb to one sentence.

Read each pair of sentences. Combine the two sentences into one sentence by adding an adjective or adverb. Write the new sentence on the line provided.

1. Mount Etna is a volcano. It is active.

   _____

   _____

2. Mount Etna is located in Sicily. Sicily is a beautiful island.

   _____

   _____

3. Mount Etna has violent eruptions. The eruptions are frequent.

   _____

   _____

4. Catania is a city in Sicily. It is crowded and bustling.

   _____

   _____

5. Regina would like to see Mount Etna. She would like to see it someday.

   _____

   _____

At Home: Have the student circle the adjectives and adverbs in the sentences above.

The Dog of Pompeii • Grade 6/Unit 6   185

Name_____

- Two sentences can be combined by adding a prepositional phrase from one sentence to the other.

Read each pair of sentences. Combine the two sentences into one sentence by adding a prepositional phrase. Write the new sentence on the line provided.

1. Regina is a scientist. She works at the University of Rome.

   _____

   _____

2. Regina works in a special department. The department was specifically formed for studying volcanic activity.

   _____

   _____

3. Italy's most famous volcano is Vesuvius. It is now dormant.

   _____

   _____

4. Mount Etna is still erupting. It spews red-hot lava on the eastern coast of Sicily.

   _____

   _____

5. The land around Mount Etna is very fertile. It is fertile because of the rich soil.

   _____

   _____

At Home: Ask the student to write two related sentences, then combine them using a prepositional phrase.

© Macmillan/McGraw-Hill

Name_____

- Capitalize the first word of every sentence and end with the correct punctuation mark.
- Use a comma before the conjunction in a compound sentence. If there is no conjunction, use a semicolon.
- Use a comma after a dependent clause at the beginning of a sentence.

Rewrite each sentence using proper capitalization, commas, and end punctuation.

1. a layer of white cloud hovered above the summit of Mount Etna it was an amazing sight

_____

_____

2. at almost thirty miles in diameter the great sloping cone of Etna is immense

_____

_____

3. etna erupts regularly its most recent eruptions have been in 1978, 1979, 1986, and 1992

_____

_____

4. sicily has about the same land mass as the state of Maryland Etna covers a large part of its eastern side

_____

_____

5. citrus farmers grow lemons and oranges on the lands around Mount Etna thanks to centuries of eruptions the soil is rich and fertile

_____

_____

_____

At Home: Ask the student to pick out the compound and complex sentences in a passage.

Name_____

- Two sentences can be combined by adding an adjective or adverb from one sentence to the other.
- Two sentences can be combined by adding a prepositional phrase from one sentence to the other.

Combine any sentences you can in the explanation below. Then rewrite the explanation, correcting any mistakes in punctuation, capitalization, or comma usage.

How to Make a Volcano at Home

In order to make a volcano at home you need baking soda. You need vinegar. You need a container to put your volcano in. Put some baking soda in the container pour in some vinegar. Watch what happens this "eruption" is called an acid base reaction. Your "volcano" really erupts! The eruption is caused by carbon dioxide. The carbon dioxide is given off as the acid in the vinegar neutralizes the sodium bicarbonate in the baking soda.

_____

_____

_____

_____

_____

_____

_____

_____

_____

_____

_____

At Home: Invite the student to write a short explanation of how to do something simple.

Name _____

Read each pair of sentences. Combine the two sentences into one sentence using adjectives, adverbs, or prepositional phrases. Then write the new sentence on the line provided.

1. Regina will be traveling soon. She will be traveling to the island of Sicily.

   _____
   _____
   _____

2. She will travel from Rome to Catania. She will travel by car.

   _____
   _____
   _____

3. Regina lives in Rome. She lives near the Coliseum.

   _____
   _____
   _____

4. Regina enjoys her life as a university professor. She enjoys it very much.

   _____
   _____
   _____

5. Volcanoes are Regina's interest. Volcanoes are her main interest.

   _____
   _____
   _____

Name _____

> • Two sentences can be combined by adding an adjective or adverb from one sentence to the other.
> • Two sentences can be combined by adding a prepositional phrase from one sentence to the other.

Combine and revise each set of sentences about the picture into one sentence. Add commas if they are necessary. Write the sentence on the line provided.

1. Mount Etna is a volcano on the island of Sicily in Italy. It is active.

   _____

   _____

   _____

2. Regina has traveled to Sicily to study the volcano. She traveled from Rome.

   _____

   _____

3. People are hurt when volcanoes erupt. They are hurt by flowing lava. They are hurt by tidal waves.

   _____

   _____

4. Regina's car moved swiftly toward the volcano. It moved along the highways of Italy.

   _____

   _____

Read the passage and look at each underlined adverb. What word does the adverb modify? Circle the letter of your answer.

Regina's trip to Sicily was <u>immediately</u> successful. She gathered her data
                                    (1)

<u>rapidly</u>. <u>Soon</u> she would take her photos and pages of notes back to Rome.
  (2)   (3)

1. **A.** successful
   B. Sicily
   C. trip
   D. was

2. **A.** She
   B. gathered
   C. data
   D. her

3. **A.** she
   B. photos
   C. take
   D. Rome

Read the passage and look at the underlined sentences. Is there a mistake? If there is, how do you correct it? Circle the letter of your answer.

<u>Nothing can't stop Regina from completing her research on Mount Etna.</u>
                                    (4)

<u>For more than six months, she has been studying the great mountain of fire the locals</u>
                                    (5)

<u>call "La Montagna."</u>

4. **A.** Change *completing* to *complete*.
   B. Change *on* to *over*.
   C. Change *can't* to *can*.
   D. No mistake.

5. **A.** Change *than* to *that*.
   B. Add a semicolon after *months*.
   C. Change *studying* to *studied*.
   D. No mistake.

At Home: Ask the student to write one sentence using an adverb.

Read the passage below and look at each underlined section. Is there a mistake? If there is, how do you correct it? Circle the letter of your answer.

The volcano looks more dangerously than Regina had expected. But Regina is not no
(6)
amateur researcher. She quickly laces up her hiking boots and begins to climb.
(7)   (8)

6. **A.** Change *volcano* to *volcano's*.
   B. Change *looks* to *looking*.
   C. Change *dangerously* to *dangerous*.
   D. No mistake.

7. **A.** Change *is* to *are*.
   B. Remove *not*.
   C. Change *researcher* to *research*.
   D. No mistake.

8. **A.** Change *quickly* to *quicker*.
   B. Change *laces* to *lacing*.
   C. Change *hiking* to *hike*.
   D. No mistake.

Look at the sentence pairs. How could each pair best be combined? Write your sentences on the lines provided.

9. The most fertile lands around Etna often yield five harvests a year. These lands are located up to about 3,000 feet.

_____

_____

_____

10. It is a large construction project. It is the largest construction project since work began on the expressway.

_____

_____

_____

At Home: Ask the student to write three sentences using adverbs, prepositions, and negatives.

© Macmillan/McGraw-Hill